HOW TO HELP AN ALCOHOLIC

THE WESTMINSTER PASTORAL AID BOOKS
Russell L. Dicks, General Editor

MY FAITH LOOKS UP, by Russell L. Dicks
YE SHALL BE COMFORTED, by William F. Rogers
THE BEST IS YET TO BE, by Paul B. Maves
SPRINGS OF LIVING WATER, by Carl J. Scherzer
HOW TO HELP AN ALCOHOLIC, by Clifford J. Earle

(*Other titles in preparation.*)

HOW TO HELP AN ALCOHOLIC

by Clifford J. Earle

Philadelphia
THE WESTMINSTER PRESS

CONTENTS

FOREWORD

THE ALCOHOLIC has been described as "the leper" of this generation. He comes to feel himself an outcast, misunderstood, criticized, and rejected. His sense of dignity sinks to a very low ebb. The one thing he knows is to escape through excessive drinking. To tell him that he is destroying himself is to increase his drinking, for basically that is what he is trying to do. To tell him that he is hurting his family and destroying their love for him is only to increase his drinking, because he feels that he has already disgraced them. To tell him to stop drinking, particularly if you are a significant person to him, is to push him farther into alcoholism because you have told him to do that which he cannot. He has lost his sense of selfhood, his sense of being of worth. His one desire is to get drunk and forget it all, and he usually does.

When I began work at the Massachusetts General Hospital in 1933, we were told in the psychiatric clinic, "You have not gained your spurs as a counselor until you have broken your heart over one drunk and one dope." The implications were that you would "break your heart"; you would not be able to help an alchoholic because he was beyond help. Fortunately that is no longer believed to be true. The Alcoholics Anonymous have demonstrated, as have an increasing number of private sanitoria, rehabilitation centers, and clinics, that the alcoholic can be helped. The picture, however, is still very dark. Alcoholism is considered the third health problem of the nation. While a great deal is known about the alcoholic and what alcohol does to the drinker, still much more is to be learned. This problem, like all health problems, is basically a problem of religion, for religion holds the key to health.

Clifford Earle has written an excellent book which offers aid to the family, the friend, the employer, and even the casual reader, to understand the person who indulges in excessive drinking. Much is being written upon this subject, but few writers have had much to say about the contribution of the church and the pastor. In this respect Clifford Earle's book is different. He writes with a clear and direct style which gives to the reader an understanding of the complicated problem; and above all there is a note of hope throughout the book. Hope is essential if the alcoholic and those who live with him and love him are to help him to regain his sense of dignity so that he can both give and receive love.

RUSSELL L. DICKS.

PART

I

HELPING ALCOHOLICS

I

THE MEASURE OF THE PROBLEM

The problem of excessive drinking becomes very real when it involves someone close to us by ties of family or friendship. His difficulty becomes our burden and concern. We want to know where the trouble lies and what we can do about it. Let us begin by considering some of the over-all dimensions of the problem.

As LONG AS PEOPLE USE alcoholic beverages there will be men and women whose drinking gets them into trouble. There will be those who become problems to themselves and to others through alcohol.

Here are several not unusual cases.

1. Orlo Smith, thirty-seven years old and unmarried, lives at home with his widowed mother and two younger sisters. At one time he had a good position in an advertising agency. He began to drink immoderately about ten years ago. His bouts with alcohol thereafter became more and more frequent and serious. About four years ago he lost his job, although his employer had been patient to an extreme, and since then he has been unable to hold a position of any kind for more than a few weeks. He has made many apparently sincere efforts to get on top of his problem, but without success. Dry interludes usually end in bad benders. His record of alcoholic achieve-

ments includes two arrests for drunken and disorderly conduct, several prolonged absences from his home, the loss of his driver's permit for operating an automobile while under the influence of alcohol, at least three periods of hospitalization because of acute intoxication, and a futile stay of several months' duration in a rest home. Family savings have been exhausted. His sisters, both employed in office positions, maintain the home.

The situation is now more desperate than ever. Hardly a day passes without Orlo's becoming at least mildly intoxicated. He used to be an attractive and likable person, generous and considerate to a fault. Now he is usually unfriendly, evasive, suspicious, and often abusive in his relationships with the members of his family. They are anxious to the point of despair as they see how prolonged excessive drinking is affecting his mental and physical health. They know that something must be done soon.

2. Henry Brown is a " hired man " on a dairy farm in the Middle West. He lives with his wife and ten-year-old son in a comfortable house near the owner's home on the farm. Henry does not drink during the week. Every Saturday, however, he goes to the nearby county-seat town, where he spends most of his time and a good deal of his money in taverns. He is usually intoxicated by the time he returns home in the evening. He drinks heavily on Sunday and often is in no shape for work for a day or two after. This has been going on for several months in spite of the pleadings of his wife and the stern warnings of his employer.

Henry repeatedly declares that he will not permit himself to get drunk when he goes to town. He promises his wife that he will not have more than one or two drinks " with the boys." But he cannot stop with one or two drinks. After each week-end binge he is remorseful and eager to make amends. His wife and son realize that, though Henry means well, he really cannot be counted on to control his drinking. They still hope that he will get hold of himself, but they are beginning to fear that the situation will grow worse rather than improve. They are worried.

3. Ethyl Jones lives in a small Texas community where her husband manages a restaurant. They have no children. They have joined a church although they do not attend Sunday services regularly. They are members of a young adult group in the church. Their principal interest, however, is golf. During most of the year they play two or three times a week at a country club to which the " best families " of the town belong.

In their country club associations, Ethyl and her husband have learned to use alcoholic beverages. Though her husband drinks discreetly, claiming that he " does not like the stuff," Ethyl frequently drinks enough to be noticeably affected. Her behavior at country club dinners and parties has sometimes embarrassed her husband. He has reason to believe that she has begun to drink at home alone. Several times recently she has been " high " when he arrived home at the end of the day. He has tried to discuss the matter with her, but she is evasive and unco-operative. He now realizes that alcohol is becoming a real problem in Ethyl's life. He wonders what he should do about it.

4. Bill Andrews is the busy and successful junior partner in a well-known law firm in an Eastern city. He lives in a comfortable suburb with his wife and two daughters, both of whom are in high school. The family are greatly interested and very active in a local church. Bill is an officer of the church; he and his wife are stalwarts in the choir.

Mrs. Andrews does not drink, and does not permit drinking in her home. However, Bill feels that it is necessary for him to drink " for business reasons." He has long been very moderate in his use of alcoholic beverages, but in recent months the occasions for drinking have steadily increased. Now they seem to occur three or four times a week. On many of these occasions Bill exceeds moderation in the amount he consumes. The resulting condition is such that he has had to miss choir practice three times in the last three months. On one of these occasions, while driving home " under the influence," he was involved in a serious and costly automobile accident.

His wife is astonished and offended by his behavior. She both scolds and pleads, but she is quite worried and wonders how she might be responsible.

5. Fred Davidson, a veteran of the Korean fighting, has recently received a medical discharge from the Army. A leg injury, now completely healed, has left him with a slight limp; otherwise he is in perfect health. He was very happy to get home, and for a time he enjoyed the fuss his parents and younger brother made over him. He co-operated in their plans to entertain him and to show him off to their friends.

That was several months ago. Now he resents being at the center of attention. He especially resents his parents' questions about what he plans to do. Breakfast time, with its queries and hints, has become an ordeal for Fred. After breakfast he usually leaves the house and does not return until evening, sometimes quite late.

Fred's mother has learned that he spends most of his time in downtown taverns and bowling alleys. He associates with a crowd of men whose reputations are not good. She has heard from a reliable source that Fred is drinking " more than is good for him," although she has observed no signs of intoxication. She is deeply distressed by all that she sees and hears about Fred's behavior. She remembers that her brother " went to pieces " after the First World War, and fears that Fred may be headed for trouble.

These accounts are based on actual case histories. They illustrate some of the ways in which the use of alcoholic beverages involves people in trouble.

Sometimes, as in the case of Orlo Smith, the situation is desperate. Here inebriety may be responsible for a series of crises — loss of employment, financial trouble, erratic behavior with unhappy social consequences, automobile mishaps, strained family relationships, a variety of physical ailments, and even psychological disorders. Alcoholism is a major source of human woe.

In some cases, as with Henry Brown, the situation is serious even though the one whose drinking causes trouble is only in the early stages of alcoholism. Unless real help is provided in a hurry, things will become much worse.

Ethyl Jones's case is representative of situations in which the danger is anticipated alcoholism. Preliminary symptoms have already appeared. Here too there is trouble ahead unless help is forthcoming.

Bill Andrews and Fred Davidson are examples of drinking patterns in which alcoholism, or uncontrolled drinking, is not presently in the picture. The related difficulties are usually relatively minor but nonetheless real. In some situations, as in Bill Andrews' case, they have an importance that makes them downright serious. One does not have to be an alcoholic, or even an inebriate, to get into trouble through drinking.

However, most of the trouble related to drinking is caused by the so-called excessive drinker — the person, man or woman, who frequently and characteristically exceeds moderation in his use of alcoholic beverages. He is the original and primary cause of complaint against alcohol.

There are approximately 115,000,000 persons of drinking age, fifteen years and older, in the United States. Of these, approximately 67,000,000 use alcoholic beverages.

The most recent studies indicate that the number of serious problem drinkers is about 5,000,000. This number includes 1,200,000 persons who are excessive drinkers without addiction and 3,800,000 who are alcoholics in various stages of alcohol addiction. Of the 5,000,000 problem drinkers in America, nearly 1,000,000 have developed various physical and mental ailments as a result of prolonged excessive drinking. It is these who are commonly called chronic alcoholics.

Present data suggest that over 7 per cent of those who use alcoholic beverages become problem drinkers. This ratio is based on current estimates of the number of excessive drinkers and the size of the drinking population. It is not a true relationship, however, because of the number of years it takes to produce an alcoholic.

A few alcohol addicts get that way within a short time, two or three years after they begin to drink. But the great majority have a drinking history of at least ten years' duration prior to the onset of addiction. In the 1940–1950 decade the number of drinkers in the United States increased by at least one third. A true index of the number of drinkers who become problem drinkers cannot be determined until the size of the drinking population, those who use alcoholic beverages, remains fairly constant for approximately ten years.

Problem drinking is much more prevalent among men than among women, the ratio being roughly seven to one — seven male alcoholics for every woman alcoholic. It has been asserted frequently that inebriety among women is increasing at a faster rate than inebriety among men. This is not true. There has been a sharp increase in the number of women alcoholics and inebriates because of the great rise in recent years in the number of people who use alcoholic beverages. But the ratio of male to female problem drinkers is slightly higher today than it was in 1940, and notably higher than in preprohibition days.

Studies reveal that problem drinking is more prevalent in large urban and industrial areas than in smaller cities under 100,000 population, and in rural communities. The rate of alcoholism — the number of alcoholics per 1,000 users of alcoholic beverages — in large cities is more than twice the rate in rural areas.

It has been observed that the rate of problem drinking within the drinking population is higher in states with a high proportion of dry sentiment than in states where the index of dry sentiment is low. This is understandable when one considers that in states where dry sentiment is high, there will very likely be relatively fewer drinkers but less casual drinking, and consequently a higher ratio of serious drinking, than in wet states.

Five million problem drinkers — that alone makes alcoholism one of the most serious public health problems in America. The situation is much more tragic than the data indicated.

Consider the five " examples " with which we began this chapter. In each instance the problem involves more persons than the one who did the drinking. In Orlo Smith's case, the lives of at least three other people were directly affected. It would not be an exaggeration to say that at least 15,000,000 persons, one in every ten of the American population, are touched by problems related to alcoholism and inebriety.

Here, truly, is the measure of the problem of alcohol.

2

HOW TO RECOGNIZE AN ALCOHOLIC

How can we be sure that a person who drinks to excess is really an alcoholic? When that person is a friend or relative, it becomes very important that we have a sound diagnosis of his condition. A great deal depends upon it — our attitude toward him, the way we approach him in offering help, the kind and amount of outside assistance we seek in dealing with the problem. It is dangerous to jump to conclusions and act hastily where alcoholism is a possibility. Let us consider some of the cardinal signs of alcohol addiction.

IT USUALLY IS NOT EASY to recognize an alcoholic. One can spot a drunk in the advanced stages of alcoholism readily enough, but the earlier stages of the affliction often escape detection. The preliminary and early symptoms are sometimes unnoticed in a person who is crossing over from uncomplicated drinking to alcoholism, even by his friends and members of his family. Not everyone who drinks heavily is an alcoholic. Some persons drink to excess because of stupidity or foolishness, or because they think it is the smart thing to do. Whatever the reason, these people can stop drinking if they want to.

An alcoholic may be described as a person with an unmanageable craving for alcohol. The outstanding criterion of the disorder is his inability, without help, to achieve permanent sobriety. He may wish to stop drinking, but he is obsessed with an unconquerable fear that without alcohol life would be impossibly difficult.

A major characteristic of alcohol addiction is the loss of control in the drinking situation. In time the alcoholic's ability to manage his drinking disappears completely. So long as he stays away from alcohol he has no difficulty, but when he begins to drink he is unable to limit himself to a moderate amount. For the time being, alcohol becomes the most important thing in his life. A spree of a day or a week or a month of uncontrolled drinking follows, and after that the hang-over.

A second important characteristic of alcoholism is the progressive nature of the disorder. The symptoms are graded. They increase in severity from stage to stage. The affliction begins as a hardly noticeable deviation from customary drinking. In time a series of more obvious and increasingly objectionable features of the disorder make their appearance. Then follow years of progressive deterioration that involves every aspect of the victim's life. The end is either death or insanity unless somewhere along the line the affliction is treated and arrested.

A third characteristic of alcohol addiction has to do with the motivation for drinking. The alcoholic drinks because he likes what alcohol does for him. He finds that it makes life seem simpler and easier, and he uses it for that purpose. Alcohol gives him immediate though temporary relief from the burden of his problems but really makes life more difficult. He ignores all this, however, as he seeks through alcohol to ease his discomfort and tension. He may not like liquor — many alcoholics don't — but he thinks he needs it in order to live.

Certain telltale symptoms in the realm of drinking behavior are sometimes useful in helping one to tell whether or not a person under observation is an alcoholic.

One indicator is the " blackout," described as temporary amnesia related to a period of intoxication. Experiencing a " blackout " is not to be confused with " passing out." A person has a " blackout " when, for example, he wakes up in the morning after a party and cannot recall where he has been or what he has done after the first few drinks. At the time, of course, neither he nor those around him are aware of anything unusual. Only later does the victim of the " blackout " realize that he has " drawn a blank." " Blackouts " are not limited to alcoholics. Even a moderate drinker who gets drunk only once in his life may experience a " blackout " on that occasion. Among alcoholics, however, " blackouts " are an almost universal occurrence. Usually they begin to happen in the very early stages of alcohol addiction. In the later stages they are often a frequent occurrence. Since a " blackout " is really a reaction to intoxication, it should not be regarded as evidence of alcoholism, but rather as a danger signal or a possible symptom.

By many little signs a potential alcoholic will reveal to an informed observer that he is beginning to lose control of his drinking. He may promise his wife that he will limit himself to two drinks in an evening, but by means of various subterfuges and excuses he will manage to have many more. He may take several quick drinks in the kitchen on the sly while pouring refreshments for guests. He may start drinking before the guests arrive and keep well ahead of everyone else in the consumption of alcohol during the evening. He may create a scene in order to have a reason for drinking more than he planned or promised to drink. However he manages it, when a person in a drinking situation intends to take a couple and winds up cockeyed, and does that persistently, he has crossed over into the early phase of alcoholism.

In the early stages of addiction, alcoholics generally make several real and sincere efforts to bring their drinking under control. A familiar technique, tried by a great majority of alcohol's victims, is " going on the water wagon." Sometimes the " water wagon " represents an attempt to stop drinking entirely. Usually, however, the alcoholic has in mind a limited period of time during which he tries not to drink. After a frightening " blackout," for example, he may venture " to lay off liquor for a couple of months " or " to quit drinking until Christmas." The " water wagon " and other forms of drinking control attempted by an alcoholic reveal that he is beginning to realize that his drinking is getting to be a problem. " Going on the wagon " is not to be regarded as a symptom of alcoholism, but rather as a clue to what is going on in the mind of a person under observation.

The " morning drink " as a regular occurrence reveals usually that a person has lost control not only in the drinking situation but also over the occasions for drinking. Upon waking in the morning an alcoholic may experience some hangover effects from yesterday's drinking — nervousness, tremor, nausea, remorse, depression. These he must quickly anesthetize with alcohol if he is to be in shape for the day. So the " morning drink " becomes for him a necessity. And more, it proves to the alcoholic that he really needs alcohol in order to be normal. Many students of the alcohol problem regard the " morning drink" as one of the cardinal signs of alcoholism. It is a symptom appearing in the drinking behavior of nearly all alcoholics.

A " bender " is described as " staying drunk for more than a day without regard for your work or your family or anything else." Occasionally a nonalcoholic heavy drinker may go on a " bender " as his way of reacting to a crisis or a disappointment. Periodic " benders," however, are a drinking behavior that is usually identified with alcoholism. They appear as a somewhat advanced symptom in the drinking histories of a large majority of alcoholics. They may happen at irregular intervals ranging from a few weeks to several months. As the affliction progresses, drinking sprees are likely to occur more frequently, to last longer, and to increase in severity. Periodic " benders " are regarded by many authorities as a major manifestation of the middle phase of alcoholism, intermediate between a primary phase characterized by loss of control, and a more advanced phase in which the alcoholic drinks to live and lives to drink.

Two other manifestations of an alcoholic's condition often appear to members of his family and to others in position to observe him closely.

First, a genuine alcoholic is usually worried about his drinking. This distinguishes him from the average heavy drinker who deliberately uses alcohol in excessive amounts and likes what happens to him. The alcohol addict drinks because he craves alcohol, and is not pleased when his drinking leads to a variety of difficulties. He cannot help noticing that he is different from his friends in the way he needs and uses alcohol. He knows that something is wrong. He insists that he is all right, but really he is worried. His anxiety often leads him to try to limit or control his drinking. He may decide, for example, to drink only before dinner. Or he may switch from one type of alcoholic beverage to another. Or he may temporarily " go on the wagon."

Secondly, his drinking in time interferes with his eating. This happens because the alcoholic is more interested in alcohol than in food. Moreover, heavy drinking may affect the taste buds so that all food " tastes like hay." His appetite all but disappears, because alcohol, with its high calorific content, satisfies most of the immediate energy requirements of the body. The failure of the alcoholic to eat right deprives the body of many of the foods that are essential to health — vitamins, carbohydrates, fats, proteins, certain minerals. These lacks in time result in actual body damage. The aging process is accelerated. Many of the physical and nervous disorders associated with chronic alcoholism, even cirrhosis of the liver and delirium tremens, are now suspected to be nutritional deficiency diseases.

Sometimes an identifying feature of alcoholism is the way it causes trouble. Excessive drinking of the kind an alcoholic does is bound to produce a persistent and growing problem in one or more areas of his life.

Most often affected, and often most seriously, is the home life of the alcoholic. His unpredictable and usually inconvenient behavior while under the influence of liquor places a heavy strain upon family ties. Domestic life is sometimes reduced to a succession of quarrels and scenes which drive the offender into either angry resentment or anguished remorse. It is not remarkable that alcoholism is an important factor in the breaking up of many homes.

Money trouble is a familiar alcoholic complication. The cost of liquor is such that a heavy drinker often spends as much as a hundred dollars a month for his beverages. If he is not an alcoholic, the chances are that he will spend only as much as he can afford. If he is an alcoholic, however, he will get his liquor even though he cannot afford it. In time his drinking will have an adverse effect upon his income, producing further financial complications. Savings are spent, insurance premiums go unpaid, jewelry and clothing are pawned, living standards go down, all because alcohol has become for its victim the most important thing in life.

Persistent and deepening problems may appear also in the social life of the alcoholic when he offends and loses his friends, in his business or professional life when he becomes erratic and inefficient in handling his work and finally loses his job, and in his personal life with the disintegration of his health.

Any one of these sets of problems would be enough to cause an average person to limit or stop his use of alcoholic beverages. For him the solution is logical and not too difficult. An alcoholic, however, may see with equal clarity that in order to straighten out his life he must cut down or cut out his drinking, but he will fail to do so because he cannot do it without help. He will keep on drinking even though he knows that his drinking causes a continuing and deepening problem.

We have suggested here some of the cardinal signs of alcoholism — the essential characteristics of the ailment, several give-away symptoms in the realm of drinking behavior, certain manifestations that may be observed by someone very close to the alcoholic, and evidence related to the problems caused by continued excessive drinking.

These signs are useful in helping one to decide whether a person under observation is or is not an alcoholic. A decision in this matter is important, for upon it depends the kind of help that is offered to the one whose drinking is causing trouble.

Relatives and close friends of a person who is suspected on good grounds of being an alcoholic should be advised of the fact in order that they may not be unfair in judging him or unwise in dealing with him. They should understand that alcoholism is an ailment, and that an alcoholic should be treated with full regard for his illness.

It should be recognized always that a layman's diagnosis of alcoholism has its dangers and limitations. Wherever possible, the counsel of experts should be sought.

3

WHERE THE PROBLEM BEGINS

If we are to be at all effective in helping someone with an alcohol problem, we must have some awareness of its nature and origin. This is especially true when the problem is alcoholism, for here quick and easy explanations often increase the difficulty. The question of moral responsibility is also involved. In the following discussion of the causes of inebriety, we shall try to be accurate without being technical.

WHEN WE ARE TALKING about intoxication, the important consideration is the amount of alcohol a person consumes or, more correctly, the amount of alcohol in his blood stream. No matter what or why a man drinks, when a certain amount of alcohol enters his blood stream, he is drunk. Intoxication usually occurs when the alcoholic content of his blood reaches a proportion of .10 to .20 per cent, 10 to 20 drops of alcohol in every 10,000 drops of blood. Thereupon he begins to show some of the familiar signs of inebriation — thickness of speech, unsteadiness of step, a boisterous or belligerent manner, incoherency of thought. These effects appear because alcohol acts as a depressant upon the central nervous system.

In habitual drunkenness the important question is not how much a person drinks but why he drinks. When a man becomes intoxicated or exceeds moderation in his use of alcoholic beverages frequently and regularly, there is a reason for it. The condition can be understood only in terms of its cause.

In some cases of chronic inebriety the principal causes are to be found in environmental and social factors. Some drink immoderately because they think it is smart or manly or a mark of distinction. They seek the approval of those who look upon this kind of behavior with favor. Some are in occupations that surround them with temptations and opportunities for heavy drinking — salesmen, promoters, entertainers, waiters, bartenders, distillery workers. Others use alcohol to compensate for sordid surroundings, for continuous frustration, or for the dreariness of life. Frequent drinking bouts bring variety and excitement into an otherwise monotonous and disappointing existence. Still others drink immoderately as a response to a crisis or catastrophe. A real difficulty in all these cases is the lack of personal standards supporting sobriety.

On the whole, however, inebriates " get that way " because of factors within themselves. They drink to excess because they cannot, without help, do otherwise. They are driven by an uncontrollable craving for alcohol. In other words, they are alcohol addicts.

A person crosses the border line between controlled drinking and addiction when he uses alcohol as an aid in adjusting to reality. He may wish to stop drinking, but he is obsessed with the fear that without alcohol he would not be able to exist. Somehow he has come to believe that he needs alcohol in order to be " normal." The urge is real and powerful. In its grip the alcoholic is incapable of thinking normally or making rational judgments about alcohol.

A large proportion of alcohol addicts, 60 per cent or more of the total number, are rather normal persons who develop an unreasonable dependence upon alcohol in the course of their drinking. That is, they are about as normal as most people when they begin to drink. They handle their worries and fears without artificial help. They discover, however, that alcohol, through its anesthetic effects, makes their problems seem simpler and easier. Through an alcoholic haze life appears rosier and happier. So they learn to use alcohol in immoderate amounts to help them to overcome anxieties and frustrations. In time their drinking becomes addictive, and often produces personality disturbances that were not originally present.

A much smaller proportion of alcohol addicts are more or less disorganized personalities to begin with, and learn to use alcohol for quick and temporary relief from their conflicts. In their cases, immoderate drinking is symptomatic of an original personality disorder, such as depressions, deep anxieties, daydreaming, and a withdrawal from the realities of their lives. Others are psychopathic personalities of whom psychiatrists despair; these are persons who have no moral sense of responsibility. Still others are handicapped by inferior mental capacities. The periodic drinker may be first a depressed person; that is, he becomes discouraged periodically, and turns to drink when he becomes depressed. The daydreamer lives in a world of his imagination and alcohol helps him to keep up his illusion.

All these persons have a hard time in adjusting themselves to life's shocks and disappointments, and learn to depend upon alcohol for relief and compensation. This leads to full-fledged addiction, in which alcohol becomes the most important thing in life. These persons should be referred to a physician and preferably to a psychiatrist, who is a doctor who specializes in treating emotional difficulties.

That alcohol addiction is basically psychological in nature, rather than physiological, is the conviction of many authorities on the subject. Prolonged heavy drinking may affect body processes, producing critical physiological changes, so as to enhance the " demand " for alcohol. But it appears in most cases that the irresistible urge to drink is related primarily to psychological factors.

Interesting light on the psychological approach to alcohol addiction comes from laboratory experiments conducted by a noted psychiatrist, Dr. Jules Massermann. Their purpose was to compare the reaction of normal and neurotic subjects to alcohol. The tests involved sixteen cats, which were taught to open a box and take food from it whenever a signal light flashed. Then they were taught to operate the light switch, a large button, when it was placed in the cage. When a cat wanted food, it would operate the switch with a paw, watch for the light, and then go to the box. Under alcoholic influence, however, it forgot how to use the switch. At this stage of the experiment alcohol had to be given to the cats by hypodermic injection, since they repudiated alcoholic milk.

In the second phase of the tests the cats were given a slight electric shock when they went to the food box. When this had happened several times, they refused to go to the box. They would not operate the switch or respond to the signal. They showed signs of deep emotional distress. The conflict between the urge to avoid pain and the hunger urge was too much for them. The cats quickly became victims of a psychological disorder, a neurosis, that paralyzed their entire behavior.

At this point the cats were once more given small amounts of alcohol by injection. When they were mildly intoxicated, they would again operate the light switch and take food from the box. As soon as the effects of the alcohol disappeared, they lapsed into their apathetic and neurotic behavior. Thereafter the cats voluntarily drank milk containing up to 10 per cent of alcohol. In fact they preferred alcoholic milk to pure milk. They could not be kept away from the " spiked " milk. The alcohol brought them relief, helped them to overcome their difficulties. They were completely dependent upon alcoholic intoxication for " normal " living.

The neurotic cats had became addicted to alcohol. The addiction was related to their neurosis; it was essentially psychological in character. When the cats were retrained so that the conflict was resolved, they no longer needed or wanted alcohol.

Like the alcoholic cats of Dr. Massermann's laboratory, there are people who crave alcohol as a means of solving their difficulties, or of reducing the feeling of discomfort arising from their inability to get on top of their troubles. Their addiction seems to be basically psychological, rooted in painful personality disturbances.

This does not mean that alcoholism has no physiological involvements. Authorities are not ruling out the possibility that a physiological peculiarity may be connected with at least some cases of addictive drinking. Many physiologists have noted the effect of excessive drinking upon the metabolic functions of the body, the ability of the body to use food. Some have observed what they believe to be a change in the functioning of the pituitary gland, located at the base of the brain, which produces many vital hormones. Recent research leads a number of physiologists to think that alcohol addiction may be related to deficiencies in the adrenal cortex, the surface layers of the adrenal glands, whose importance in maintaining the health of the body is now known.

A few authorities go so far as to insist that alcoholism is due entirely to an organic deficiency of some kind. They claim that when the exact nature of the trouble has been identified, medical science probably will be able to provide a sure-fire medical

cure for the disorder. This view seems to overlook the find-
ings of psychologists and psychiatrists who have studied the
problem.

It is probable that a biological factor of some sort may eventually be found that increases a person's chances of becoming
an alcoholic. But that is not the whole story. The total personality is involved, and at present it appears that an approach
that emphasizes psychological factors is at once sound and
practical.

Some persons who are addicted to drinking speak of their
condition as an allergy to alcohol. This may be a useful de-
scription but it is really quite inaccurate. An allergy is defined as a hypersensitivity to a substance, an abnormal physical reaction. An allergy to certain pollens, for example, causes
the uncomfortable symptoms that we call hay fever. A person
who is allergic to oranges cannot eat that delightful fruit without experiencing unusual reactions, such as swollen and in-
flamed tissues, fever, and nausea. A few people are allergic to
alcohol in the same way. But alcohol addiction is not in any
way an allergic reaction.

Often one hears alcoholics compare their condition with
diabetes, but here again the reference is mistaken and mislead-
ing. In the disease commonly called diabetes the ability of the
body to use sugar is impaired. The victim of the disorder must
balance his intake of sugar with his body's power to consume
it. He cannot eat sweets indiscriminately without serious consequences. It is tempting to say that the alcoholic cannot drink
like other people just as the diabetic cannot eat candy like
other people. But the two disorders are entirely different both
as to what causes them and how they affect their victims. They
cannot be compared.

The question of heredity is often raised in discussions of excessive drinking and alcoholism. So-and-so is an alcoholic, people may say, because his father was one before him. Reliable authorities agree, however, that alcohol addiction is not an inheritable affliction. There is no known cellular or metabolic peculiarity, biologically transmitted from parents to children, to explain why one person becomes an alcoholic and another person in similar circumstances does not. What are inherited in some cases are personality tendencies and constitutional instabilities that may make a person more ready for the alcoholic process. It may be true that the children of inebriate parents develop addiction more frequently than the children of non-inebriate parents, but the explanation is found in environmental and social factors.

Sometimes the statement is made that alcoholism occurs because alcohol is a habit-forming drug. True, the habit-forming potentialities of alcohol come into play in the process by which some drinkers become alcohol addicts. But their role is minor. Other factors are much more important. It should be remembered that the majority of persons who drink regularly do not become addicted. Moreover, an important distinction should be made between a narcotic drug, such as morphine, and alcohol, which is an anesthetic, in their action in the body. The repeated use of morphine and other true drugs builds up a tolerance in the human system so that larger and larger amounts are needed to produce a given effect. This does not happen in the use of alcohol. After years of excessive drinking a given amount of alcohol will affect a person in about the same way as it did when he began to drink. His ability " to hold his liquor " may appear to be improved because he has learned to manage better the obvious symptoms of intoxication. Experience has taught him what he can do and what he cannot do when he is " under the influence." But he is as drunk as ever.

All that we have been saying here about how the alcoholic gets that way underlines the fact that he is not a well person. He is the victim of an insidious and progressive disorder that in time affects every phase of his life.

Attempts to deal with alcoholism as though it were simply or primarily a moral problem fail repeatedly because they are based on a tragic misunderstanding of the real nature of the ailment. Whatever blame may attach to a person's behavior before the onset of addiction, when he becomes an alcoholic and cannot control his drinking good sense and Christian compassion require that he should be treated as a sick person rather than a sinner.

Here is a young man, for example, who is clearly an alcohol addict. He is a sick person, desperately in need of help. He is sick physically from malnutrition related to drinking. He is sick emotionally as a result of prolonged anxiety mixed with feelings of guilt. He is sick economically through his inability to hold a job. He is sick socially in that his friends have deserted him and his family has virtually "given him up." He truly wants to stop drinking but is driven by an irresistible obsession that he needs alcohol in order to live. He just cannot stop drinking. What this young man needs is not punishment for the crime of habitual drunkenness, but treatment based on understanding and sympathy.

4

MODERN TREATMENT FOR ALCOHOLISM

Alcoholics can be helped. Let that word sink into the consciousness of everyone who is anxious about the uncontrolled drinking of a friend or relative. There is much that authorities still need to know about alcoholism, but they know enough to offer real help. Here is a layman's outline of some of the remedies now available.

IT HAS BEEN CUSTOMARY FOR SOCIETY in the past to treat inebriates as criminals. In colonial times they were placed in stocks for public exhibition and ridicule, and often flogged. In more recent times they have been fined or jailed with thieves, prostitutes, and vagrants.

An important study of drunkenness made by the Massachusetts state legislature in 1945 included several case histories of habitual drunkards. One was a woman alcoholic, born in 1871, arrested for drunkenness for the first time in April, 1910, and arrested on similar charges in July and September of the same year. By 1937, when she was admitted to a state hospital for the mentally ill, she had been arrested for drunkenness 109 times, an average of 4 times a year. The record suggests that long before 1937 she needed something quite different from punishment for the crime of inebriation.

Local governments in America still spend an estimated $25,000,000 every year on the maintenance of " drunk tanks " in city and county jails. The waste is doubly tragic because such treatment is actually worse than useless in mitigating the problem of inebriety. For an alcoholic to be thrown into jail to sober up usually aggravates the very conditions that are in large part responsible for his dependence upon alcohol. Yet this is the only " institutional treatment " that 60 per cent of America's alcoholics ever receive.

In the last few years, however, a great deal has been written and said to inform the public of the true nature of alcoholism, and to promote a practical and compassionate approach to the problem. Enlightened courts and police departments in many cities have sought to alter the old pattern and to set up remedial services. Public-spirited citizens have encouraged a new attitude and approach based on an understanding of the alcoholic's real needs.

Between 30 and 40 states have instituted programs, or are planning to do so in the very near future, directed toward the treatment of alcoholism. In many of our larger cities public clinics for alcoholics have been set up with both public and private funds. Treatment facilities and rehabilitation projects of various kinds are now to be found in a great many communities. These multiplying services reflect a changing public attitude toward alcoholism and its victims.

Treatments for alcoholism can be roughly classified under four headings: medical, aversion, psychiatric, and religious. Religious treatment may be of the religious conversion type, or it may be pastoral counseling, which utilizes many of the insights of psychiatry as well as of pastoral experience.

Medical attention is usually required in the acute stages of alcoholism, when the victim has been drinking heavily for several days. He is suffering dreadfully, and is in no condition to do anything effective about his immediate condition except to keep on drinking. He is very much in need of help. Medical therapy does not propose to cure the alcoholic. Its purpose is to sober him up, get the alcohol out of his system, and repair some of the damage done to his body by excessive drinking. The program is usually intensive and of short duration, approximately four or five days. Its great value is in preparing the patient, both mentally and physically, for further programs of recovery and rehabilitation.

An almost universal need in the treatment of alcoholics at this stage is vitamin replacement. A concomitant of nearly all prolonged heavy drinking is vitamin deficiencies due to the fact that the drinker is more interested in alcohol than in food. Proteins and liver extract are usually required. The treatment often includes the administration of glucose. Insulin and oxygen are used as needed. Rest and proper diet are always emphasized.

In a number of clinics and treatment centers doctors are now employing endocrine therapy with very good results. This approach involves the use of adrenal cortex extract (ACE) and related drugs. The treatment, which focuses upon the acute stages of alcoholism, has produced some dramatic recoveries. The agony and shock of the hang-over have been greatly reduced, and the organic functions of the body restored to normal in a matter of hours. The endocrine approach appears to be very promising.

A major frustration for both doctors and families who are seeking to provide medical help for problem drinkers is the lack of sufficient hospital facilities. Many hospitals accept no responsibility for alcoholics. They insist that their services are " for sick people, not for drunks." Yet in the medical treatment of acute alcoholism hospitalization is usually desirable.

In " conditioned reflex " or " aversion " treatment the purpose is to induce in the patient a strong dislike of alcohol. A

generation ago one of the most popular forms of this treatment was the famous Keeley Cure developed in a private institution for alcoholics in Illinois. The Keeley Institution, still in
business, now uses a number of methods, both medical and
psychiatric.

In most of these treatments, drugs of various kinds are used
to produce acute nausea at the time the patient consumes an
alcoholic beverage. The reaction is sufficiently violent and the
timing is such that the smell and taste of alcohol will be associated thereafter in the patient's mind with the attack of
nausea. The " cure " produces a strong disposition toward
sobriety, but its effect is not lasting. The induced aversion
eventually wears off, and unless something effective is done to
reinforce the patient's will to stay sober, he usually " falls off
the wagon." In combination with psychotherapy, however, the
aversion and conditioned reflex approaches are often very
useful.

A new drug that offers interesting possibilities in alcoholic
therapy is tetraethylthiuramdisulphide (TETD), generally
known by its American trade name, Antabus. Its use in the
treatment of alcoholism has many similarities to aversion therapy. The presence of Antabus in the system produces an
allergy-like sensitivity to alcohol. The drug itself causes no
reaction, but after taking it a person cannot drink without extremely unpleasant consequences. The disagreeable reaction is
mild when a small amount of alcohol is consumed, but grows
in violence when the amount is increased. When a large quan-
tity of alcohol is involved, the reaction may be dangerously
severe. Antabus is effective in producing a reaction to alcohol
for a rather short period of time, usually from one to five days.
The effect is not permanent, as was implied in some news-
paper accounts of the discovery of the drug in 1949. Antabus
should always be used in minimal amounts as prescribed by a

qualified physician. Excessive doses have been known to aggravate neurotic and psychotic symptoms.

The use of Antabus appears to be limited to persons who are in good physical and mental condition, who give their full consent to the treatment, and who know what they are doing when they accept the drug. The treatment can succeed only with the complete co-operation of the patient. Antabus is not a cure for alcoholism. It does not remove the urge to drink. But in many cases its use can open the way for other therapies that get at the root of the trouble.

The fact that psychological factors are involved in alcohol addiction suggests immediately that psychotherapy should be useful in helping its victims. In a great many cases, alcoholics do not need psychiatric treatment in order to stop drinking. However, there are many problem drinkers who do need the ministry of psychiatry before they can arrest their drinking. Many others seek psychiatric help, even though they no longer drink, in order to establish themselves more firmly in sobriety.

Psychiatric treatment consists of a series of conversations between the alcoholic and the psychiatrist. The patient does the talking, while the doctor asks searching questions and makes quiet suggestions as to possible courses of action. These the patient may wish to try out, making his own decisions. The doctor gives very few direct orders. Rather, he tries to maintain the position of helping the patient to solve his own problems.

By means of psychiatric therapy, a person comes to a better understanding of himself and of his behavior. He may discover, for example, that he is unhappy in his job, not because of the people he works with, but because the work itself is unsuited to his abilities and disposition. He may learn that he resents his relatives, not because of something they did to him, but because of his own failure to live up to their hopes for him. He may find that his troubles have largely been brought about by his drinking, and that when he stops drinking they will in time solve themselves. Or he may discover that the trouble is deep-rooted and that a careful solution will have to be worked out with the doctor's help before he can achieve inner peace and stability.

In a number of alcoholic clinics, group therapy is now available as a form of psychiatric treatment. Several persons with similar problems meet regularly with a psychiatrist or a psychiatrically trained counselor. He leads the discussion in which the patients themselves do most of the talking. The leader asks questions and makes suggestions. His purpose is to help the patients to understand themselves and their problems, and to find workable solutions.

Psychiatric diagnosis should not be confused with psychiatric treatment. In diagnostic interviews the psychiatrist, by means of carefully ordered questions, seeks background knowledge of the patient and his problems. This enables him to know the nature of the patient's illness and his need of treatment. Two or three interviews are not considered to be adequate treatment.

A clear distinction should be made between psychiatric treatment and psychoanalysis. The latter involves a much deeper probing into the patient's mind. Psychoanalysts rarely accept alcoholic patients unless they have been dry for some time. The process of analysis can be deeply disturbing to the patient, and if he is an active alcoholic, the experience may cause him to seek relief in alcohol. However, psychoanalysis can help a recovered alcoholic to understand some of his inner problems that are too deep and obscure to respond to simpler treatments.

In all psychotherapy, the full co-operation of both the patient and his family is a necessity. Most psychiatrists prefer to keep their patients in a sanitarium, especially during the early phases of the treatment.

Religion is a major aid in the treatment of alcoholism. It is not just another alcohol therapy, however, as though one could choose between a religious treatment and a medical or psychiatric treatment. Rather, it is an approach that takes into account the spiritual aspects of personality and the religious resources for successful living.

The religious approach to alcoholism is dramatically demonstrated in the work of the Salvation Army and of " rescue missions " across the land. Often they minister to " skid row " alcoholics, homeless and sometimes hopeless men and women who have drifted beyond the reach of ordinary means of help. The stories are epic. They have taken men whose lives have been wrecked by alcohol, cleaned them up, cured them of their ailments, inspired them with faith and courage, given them a high purpose to live for, and restored them to sober and useful living. Observing some of these miraculous changes, we can only stand back and wonder at the grace of God.

The healing ministry of religion is not limited to those alcoholics who touch bottom. Faith is a resource for the problem drinker in every phase of his disorder if only he knows how to have it and to use it. Every day there are men in every stage of alcoholic addiction who achieve recovery by " turning their lives over to God."

Increasingly ministers and religious leaders of every faith are developing and demonstrating counseling skills by which they are able to give effective aid to the victims of alcohol. Many ministers are uncomprehending and unsympathetic when an alcoholic turns to them for help, but their number is diminishing. Churches are waking up to their responsibility in this field of great need. Extending its full assistance to alcoholics and their families would seem to be a normal expression of Christian concern, a pastoral service that every church should be alert and eager to render.

The most extensive modern use of religious insights and methods in helping problem drinkers is made by Alcoholics Anonymous. The amazing story of the AA fellowship and program is told in another chapter. Most modern alcoholic clinics are not limited to any one kind of treatment. They provide medical and psychiatric therapy as required. They often have a working relationship with Alcoholics Anonymous in which religious resources are used.

Treatment programs for the alcoholic are based on the conviction that (1) he needs help, (2) he can be helped. The goal is permanent recovery in which the alcoholic understands and accepts the fact that he no longer can drink.

5

ALCOHOLICS ANONYMOUS

The most extensive and successful agency working for the recovery of problem drinkers is Alcoholics Anonymous. It is essential for the family and friends of alcoholics to know what AA is and how it works. The nearly 4,000 groups across the land bring the AA program within reach of most of us. Here is a resource upon which we can call for advice and help in dealing with a person whose drinking is out of control.

THE UNIQUE FEATURE of Alcoholics Anonymous is that it is composed entirely of alcoholics — recovered alcoholics and those who are on the way to full recovery.

AA was born in 1935, when two men, a stockbroker and a physician, met in Akron, Ohio. Both men were alcoholics who had achieved a measure of recovery by the conscientious personal application of certain religious principles. They braced each other in their rather shaky sobriety, and then set themselves to the task of devising a discipline or program by which alcoholics generally could surmount their problem. The result was the "Twelve Steps to Recovery," appearing in 1938, on which the AA fellowship and program are based.

The movement started slowly. In 1939 it had no more than 100 members in three struggling groups in Akron, Cleveland, and New York. It did not even have a name. Then the two men who originated the idea and who are known jointly as the founders wrote a book about it in which they described their experiences and the methods by which early members of the groups achieved sobriety. The book, *Alcoholics Anonymous,* gave the movement both name and fame. In the last decade the growth of AA has been phenomenal. There are now an estimated 120,000 members of groups in nearly 4,000 communities in America, and active units in a growing number of other nations.

There are no national officers of AA, no constitution, no rules beyond the original Twelve Steps and a set of traditions based on experiences over the years. There is a " national headquarters " in New York, but no centralized authority. A board of nine trustees, organized as the Alcoholic Foundation, manages the general funds and provides literature and other services for local groups to use as they desire. The Foundation also assists by mail and counsel in the formation of new AA groups, and takes care of all matters of public relations. The AA program in all its aspects is financed by the contributions of its members. The principle of self-help has made the society refuse all offers of financial assistance from outside. An attractive and readable monthly magazine, *The A.A. Grapevine,* is published under the sponsorship and control of the Foundation.

A local AA group starts when two recovered alcoholics get together and try to help a third person, using the Twelve Steps as the basis of the effort. The most successful AA groups generally have from 25 to 50 members. In cities with several hundred members neighborhood groups are organized to facilitate fellowship and participation for everyone. Every group is a loosely knit voluntary fellowship of alcoholics, whose purpose in coming together is to help one another to live sober and useful lives. Men and women of all ages, from eighteen to eighty, belong to AA. They come from all sorts of backgrounds, from poor homes and rich homes, and from every profession and occupation.

Local groups have a minimum of officers. Weekly closed meetings are held in which members tell their stories, discuss their experiences, and hear occasional talks by specialists or visiting AA members on some phase of the problem of alcoholism. Frequent open meetings are held to which the public is invited. Always the Twelve Steps are emphasized as the basis of all that AA is and does.

The group usually meets in some easily accessible hall or room that is rented for the purpose or provided for its use. Many groups use facilities provided by churches, although they cannot be " sponsored " by churches or by any other organizations. AA groups often meet in libraries, police stations, fire houses, municipal buildings, and other public places. In a growing number of cities several AA groups jointly own or rent a building of modest size in which they maintain a round of central activities and services in keeping with their purpose, such as alcoholic clinics, reading rooms, recreation facilities, and classes. In our larger cities AA maintains hospital facilities for the care of alcoholics.

AA is not affiliated with any other organization or movement, even those that are working toward similar ends. It takes no sides in the wet-dry controversy. It espouses no causes. Its single aim is to help alcoholics to achieve sobriety.

The Twelve Steps to Recovery are outlined in *Alcoholics Anonymous* as follows:

1. We admitted that we were powerless over alcohol — that our lives had become unmanageable.

2. We came to believe that a Power greater than ourselves could restore us to sanity.

3. We made a decision to turn our will and our lives over to the care of God as we understood him.

4. We made a searching and fearless moral inventory of ourselves.

5. We admitted to God, to ourselves, and to another human being the exact nature of our wrongs.

6. We were entirely ready to have God remove all these defects of character.

7. We humbly asked him to remove our shortcomings.

8. We made a list of all persons we had harmed and became willing to make amends to them all.

9. We made direct amends to such people whenever possible, except when to do so would injure them or others.

10. We continued to take personal inventory, and when we were wrong, promptly admitted it.

11. We sought through prayer and meditation to improve our conscious contact with God as we understood him, praying only for knowledge of his will for us and the power to carry that out.

12. Having had a spiritual awakening as the result of these steps, we tried to carry this message to alcoholics and practice these principles in all our affairs.

The importance of the first step cannot be overemphasized. It is characteristic of an alcohol addict to insist for a long time after the onset of his trouble that he really can stop drinking if he wants to. With real reluctance and dismay does he come to acknowledge the serious nature of his drinking and his inability to cope with the problem. Yet the program of recovery cannot get started until the alcoholic admits, at least to himself, that he needs help, that he cannot go on alone. He must drop all pride and pretension on the subject of his use of alcoholic beverages.

In the second and third steps the alcoholic is led to surrender his will and life " to the care of God " as his only hope. Often he has built up a strong resistance to religious appeals based on exhortation and censure. In the context of the Twelve Steps, however, the appeal for spiritual commitment is more convincing and attractive. An alcoholic does not have to be religiously susceptible in order to use the AA discipline. The most cynical and irreligious have come, through AA, to recognize the working in their lives of a Power greater than themselves.

The next seven steps, four through ten, point the way to moral cleansing and regeneration. Here too there is no room for self-deception and pride. The eighth and ninth steps, calling for restitution for trouble and injury inflicted upon others, are unique, even among the spiritual disciplines of religious societies. They are hard to take, but exceedingly valuable in reinforcing an alcoholic's commitment to a new way of life grounded in sobriety and service.

The eleventh step calls for diligence in prayer and meditation. Here the alcoholic is admonished not to be self-centered or self-seeking in his praying, as though by prayer he could get his own way, but to pray rather for knowledge of God's will and for power to carry out that will. This is quite different from the kind of praying to which some alcoholics are accustomed.

The twelfth step challenges the alcoholic to help himself by helping others. AA groups usually place a great deal of emphasis upon this step in the program of recovery. They expect their members to give this service first claim upon their time. Often they set up classes or discussions on " twelfth-stepping." The sincerity and diligence of AA members in this part of the program account for the great growth of the movement in the last few years.

With slight adaptation the Twelve Steps of AA could be used as an outline of religious experience. The large degree of local decision and autonomy in AA means that in some groups the spiritual aspects of the program are stressed more than in other groups.

A minister in Philadelphia learned that his younger brother, living in Missouri, had started to drink and had rather quickly shown evidences of alcoholism. The minister got in touch with an AA group in his city; a contact was made by telephone with an AA group in St. Louis; in less than twenty-four hours two AA members from St. Louis had driven one hundred miles to see the young man whose drinking had got out of control. Within a few months the young man himself was a cofounder of a new AA group in his own town.

This story, though a bit unusual, illustrates the readiness with which AA seeks to bring its message of hope to victims of alcohol. AA members usually work in pairs. If an alcoholic really wants to get well, they will go to great lengths to help him, especially during the early period of recovery, when the candidate for sobriety may experience several relapses into his old drinking patterns. They are on beck and call at any hour of the day or night, always ready to give sympathetic and understanding help, to assist with family problems, even to stay with their friend when the going is rough. They are able to help because they talk the same language as the alcoholic victim; they know the problem from the inside. They assure the alcoholic that recovery is possible, explain the AA program, take him to an AA meeting, and get him started on the road to new health and happiness. In a short time, if all goes well, the initiate is teamed with a more experienced member of AA in an effort to help another alcoholic to achieve recovery.

As to the effectiveness of the AA program, it is estimated

that between 50 and 60 per cent of those who try it are permanently helped. It should be kept in mind that a large proportion of all alcoholics are " primary " addicts — that is, their difficulty is an original and fundamental personality disorder that, in most cases, cannot be helped by anything less than prolonged psychiatric treatment. Moreover, many who " try " the AA discipline never get through the first of the Twelve Steps, and cannot be said to have made a conscientious effort.

At the first national meeting of Alcoholics Anonymous, held in Cleveland in the summer of 1950, a set of Twelve Traditions was adopted. These Traditions, suggested by the experience of many AA groups over the last decade, reveal something of the dynamic and spirit of the movement:

1. Our common welfare should come first; personal recovery depends upon AA unity.

2. For our group purpose there is but one ultimate authority — a loving God as he may express himself in our group conscience. Our leaders are but trusted servants — they do not govern.

3. The only requirement for AA membership is a desire to stop drinking.

4. Each group should be autonomous, except in matters affecting other groups or AA as a whole.

5. Each group has but one primary purpose — to carry its message to the alcoholic who still suffers.

6. An AA group ought never to endorse, finance, or lend the AA name to any related facility or outside enterprise lest problems of money, property, and prestige divert us from our primary spiritual aim.

7. Every AA group ought to be fully self-supporting, declining outside contributions.

8. Alcoholics Anonymous should remain forever nonprofes-

sional, but our service centers may employ special workers.

9. AA, as such, ought never to be organized; but we may create service boards or committees directly responsible to those whom they serve.

10. Alcoholics Anonymous has no opinion on outside issues; hence the AA name ought never to be drawn into public controversy.

11. Our public relations policy is based on attraction rather than promotion; we need always to maintain personal anonymity at the level of press, radio, and films.

12. Anonymity is the spiritual foundation of all our Traditions, ever reminding us to place principles above personalities.

An interesting technique used by many AA newcomers is the "twenty-four-hour plan." Here the alcoholic proposes to keep from drinking for one day at a time. He is dismayed when he thinks that he must keep away from alcohol for the rest of his life. But twenty-four hours he knows he can manage. And so he goes on, one day at a time, for weeks on end, until he feels secure in his new way of life.

One cannot help being impressed with this simple technique as a way of handling many human frailties and weaknesses other than alcohol addiction.

6

WHAT NOT TO DO

It is not easy to extend help to an alcoholic. Often the methods used by friends and relatives of an afflicted person serve only to aggravate the condition they were intended to relieve. Extreme care and tact are required in avoiding the mistakes that are commonly made in dealing with an alcoholic. This chapter could well be entitled, "How to help by not following our impulses."

RECOVERED ALCOHOLICS OFTEN TALK disparagingly about the " home treatment " they received in the years when their alcoholism was active. They have dismal recollections of the fumbling efforts of their desperate and harassed families to help them.

Often the methods used by friends and relatives of an alcoholic " to bring him to his senses " reflect abysmal ignorance of the real nature of alcoholism. They assume, as do most people, that the wildly intemperate drinking of the alcoholic is pretty much a matter of " will power," that he could straighten up if he really applied himself to it. They believe that he is perfectly able to control his drinking, and that he fails to do so because he is irresponsible or bad or stubborn or stupid. So they argue, wheedle, trick, or force him into this or that solution of his problem. These methods fail because they are based on a misunderstanding of the alcoholic and his need.

To be sure, an alcoholic's behavior is often so exasperating that the people around him are strongly tempted to react hastily and impulsively in ways that are decidedly unhelpful. It takes grace and patience not to do the wrong things.

Those who are in a position to influence an alcoholic should never belittle or embarrass him for his inability to control his drinking.

Many people still seem to think that drinking is a manly art, that anyone who cannot or does not drink is a weakling or a " panty-waist." This belief is a hang-over, if one may use that word here, of an ancient myth that identified intoxicating beverages with life and strength. To think that way today is ridiculous. To taunt a person who is unable to drink safely can have tragic consequences.

In some circles drinking is associated with hospitality in such a way as to create a real problem for the person who cannot drink without harm. A host will press a drink upon his guests with rude insistence. He will often seem to resent anyone's attempt to say " No." For many an alcoholic struggling to stay on top of his problem, an inconsiderate host has been his ruination.

In these modern days when we know so much about alcohol and alcoholism, when there are multiplying reasons for abstinence, it should be perfectly easy for anyone to choose not to drink. It should be no more difficult or strange for one to refuse to drink or to prefer a nonalcoholic beverage than it is to refuse a cigarette or to choose tea instead of coffee.

One should never scold, entreat, or threaten an alcoholic on account of his drinking. Indeed, any form of argument is worse than useless unless the person afflicted with alcoholism is ready, by his own admission, to talk things over with someone. And even then one should avoid censure.

Scolding and preaching are out of order because they reveal a clear lack of understanding of the real state of affairs. The truth is that the alcoholic is perfectly aware of the tragic consequences of his drinking and is burdened with a sense of guilt to a degree that those around him can hardly appreciate. He knows how badly he has done. His remorse is genuine and is often so acute that the only way he can handle it is to put it to sleep with more alcohol. Scolding makes matters worse by reminding the alcoholic of his failings and really accentuating his " need " for alcohol. Moreover, he deeply resents the " holier-than-thou " attitude that is a frequent accompaniment of the morality lecture.

Pleading with an alcoholic to do better is really not greatly different from scolding him for doing badly, and is equally futile. Coaxing may appear to bring results for a time, but the alcoholic will not be able to follow through, and the last state may be worse than the first.

Threats are useless unless they are in the nature of reasonable warnings that will surely be carried out if the alcoholic persists in his intemperate way. A wife, for example, may warn her alcoholic husband that unless he straightens up and behaves she will leave him. The warning is justified if she is convinced that such drastic action is required unless things change, and is determined to carry out her threat. If he fails to heed her warning and she fails to leave him, threats thereafter will be meaningless. To threaten an alcoholic is often to provide him with a further excuse for drinking.

Any attempt to talk to an alcoholic in a way that reflects censure or incrimination merely confirms his belief that the people around him, even those who love him, do not understand his problem. And in that he is often right.

One should never call in an outsider to remonstrate with an alcoholic. A woman whose husband has become a problem drinker may be tempted to ask her minister or a trusted family friend " to tell him what he is doing to me." Usually the impulse comes when the husband is in no condition " to be reasoned with " about anything. If she should follow her impulse, her husband probably would interpret her action as an effort to get someone on her side in a family dispute, or as an attempt to shame him by showing him up at his worst. He probably would react with angry resentment or sullen defiance. And if the minister or friend should be foolish enough to do as she proposes, not only would he fail in his effort, but he would make it virtually impossible for him ever again to be in a position to be of help.

One may seek comfort and counsel from an outsider when a situation becomes so difficult as to be almost unbearable, but nothing should be done that would aggravate the problem or would close off a source of real help when the break comes.

It is usually futile for a family to tamper with the liquor stock of an alcoholic member of the household. When he is " hitting the bottle," his need is so desperate as to render useless any attempt to control the situation by shutting off the supply of alcoholic beverage.

Hiding the liquor or locking it up or pouring it down the sink often fail because the alcoholic has already anticipated such action by providing his own secret supply. Withholding money is sometimes possible, but the alcoholic nearly always finds some way to overcome the handicap even though it means pawning his best suit. He will usually exhibit unexpected courage and cunning in getting the alcohol he feels he must have in spite of everything his family does to outwit him. He may even enjoy the excitement of the contest.

Sometimes a family may try to help an alcoholic by asking his friends never to serve him liquor. The intention may be good, but the end is often far worse than the beginning. An alcoholic is extremely sensitive about his condition, and for him to be offered ginger ale while others are having cocktails is a humiliation that may have disastrous results.

In all these efforts to handle the situation, the frantic family succeeds only in becoming a " house divided against itself." By trying to force a solution upon an alcoholic, the other members of the household erect a wall of estrangement between themselves and him.

In trying to help an alcoholic one should never appear to encourage him in his drinking. Sometimes the wife of an incipient alcoholic, who herself has been an abstainer, will begin to drink with her husband " in order to keep him from drinking too much." She argues that it is better for him to drink at home with her to watch and set the pace than to spend his time " with the boys " in a local tavern. This may seem to have a good effect for a while, but in the long run it simply gives him another excuse for drinking. He is bound to see through her scheme and to resent her efforts to keep him away from his friends. And if she should ever remind him in an impulsive moment that his drinking caused her to break her rule of abstinence, the situation might well get out of bounds.

Under no circumstances should one employ medicinal remedies of the " home cure " variety in helping an alcoholic to achieve sobriety.

There was a time when the country was flooded with " quack " drugs and medicines about which outlandish claims were made as to their ability to stop the " drink habit." Many of them were in the form of pills that could be secretly dropped into a cup of coffee or even a glass of whisky for the unsuspecting alcoholic to consume. A widely used "home cure" consisted of thirty-two bottles of liquid that were to be used in sequence in carefully prescribed ways. Some "patented" drugs were said to eliminate the "allergic reaction" to alcohol.

Various brands of specially treated liquors that are supposed to be nonintoxicating or non-habit-forming have been peddled in rather recent times to the bewildered and gullible families of alcoholics. From most of these beverages certain impurities have been removed, such as fusel oil and traces of various aldehydes, but the alcoholic content is unchanged. In relation to intoxication and alcoholism they are just as potent and just as dangerous as untreated liquors.

Federal laws now keep most of these fraudulent concoctions out of the mails and off the market. But homemade remedies are still abundant. "Sure-fire" formulas are bandied about in every bar and tavern. The anxious family of an alcoholic may be strongly tempted to try them out, often without the knowledge or permission of the one whose drinking is causing trouble. But there is no easy homemade short cut to sobriety. To depend upon these cures is to invite failure and disappointment.

In all these suggestions about what not to do in trying to help an alcoholic there is a recurring theme — the admonition that nothing should be done that would make him resent or distrust a person who may someday be in a position to help him. To maintain his belief that you are his friend is of utmost importance. The time will come, perhaps sooner than one may dare to hope or expect, when the alcoholic sufferer admits that he no longer can cope with his problem alone and needs someone near and ready to whom he can turn for help.

When that day comes may you be prepared.

7

SOME POSITIVE STEPS TO TAKE

*Warnings about the things we should not do in our
relations with an alcoholic are quite necessary. To leave
the matter there, however, would be frustrating and de-
feating. When the alcoholic sufferer is someone of whom
we think a great deal, we cannot be satisfied with a solely
negative approach in our desire to help him. Let us consider some of the things we can do, the positive steps we
can take.*

INFORMATION ABOUT ALCOHOLISM is a prerequi-
site for anyone who tries to do something with or for an alcoholic. Sometimes it is a matter of life and death importance for
the husband or wife of a sufferer from alcoholism to become
informed on the subject.

Fortunately there is a growing abundance of dependable
literature about alcoholism and alcohol addicts. A few years
ago this was not the case. In the last several years, however, a number of important nontechnical books have made
their appearance. Helpful articles on the subject have appeared
in leading magazines. Most public libraries are able to furnish
an inquirer with reliable reading material.

In some 50 or 60 cities across the country local committees
on alcoholism have been formed. In the main they are branches
of The National Committee on Alcoholism, headquartered in
New York (New York Academy of Medicine Building, 2 East

103d Street). Local committees are in position to give information, provide literature, and recommend treatment facilities in the community. In 30 or more cities, committees have set up information centers staffed by trained persons who are able to counsel and assist families in dealing with the many difficult problems posed by alcoholism. These centers are an exceedingly important source of information about alcoholics and their illness. Consult the local telephone book for the address of the nearest alcoholic information center. If none is listed, call the local health board, or write to The National Committee on Alcoholism in New York.

Open meetings of Alcoholics Anonymous are another resource for persons seeking information about alcohol addiction. AA groups are within easy reach of most people who wish to know how the problem appears from the inside. Even though one must travel a considerable distance in order to attend an open meeting, the effort is worth-while. No matter how much a person may have read about alcoholism, he will learn a great deal by listening to recovered alcoholics tell their stories. He will have a deeper understanding of alcoholic behavior. Visiting an AA meeting will often make it possible for one to talk with the husband or wife of an AA member — an invaluable experience for a person in a similar relationship to an active alcoholic. AA groups in your town are sure to be listed in the local telephone book. If none is listed, write to the General Service Headquarters of AA in New York (P.O. Box 459, Grand Central Annex) for information about the nearest group.

In many communities there are ministers who are prepared to counsel with a person seeking to be informed about alcoholism. It is still true, of course, that some members of the clergy have very little understanding of the subject. Indeed, they may have ideas about it that make them considerably less than helpful in advising others. But an increasing number of ministers are genuinely interested in helping alcoholics and have acquired a good deal of practical knowledge about the problem. They are able at least to direct the inquirer to the kind of information he ought to have concerning alcoholism.

Another prerequisite, along with information about alcoholism, is a positive attitude toward the alcoholic. It is extremely important for anyone in a position to help to think of him as being ill and to deal with him accordingly.

When a person is suffering, let us say, from a nervous illness, it is customary for those around him to help him to recognize his condition and to encourage him to do something about it. His behavior at times may be difficult, but they try to understand it as being related to his affliction. They are not negative in their attitude toward the one who is ill. They do not reproach him or make him feel ashamed for being that way. As wisely as they know how, with all the care and consideration that the situation demands, they endeavor to bring the sufferer to a realization of his need for help and to a willingness to seek help. They deal with him constantly in the spirit of sympathetic understanding and concern.

In the same comprehending and considerate spirit we ought to regard the alcoholic in our midst. Our attitude toward him must be consonant with the idea that alcoholism, whatever its cause, is an ailment by which a person is unable to control his drinking. We should remember that an alcoholic is an ill person who needs help, that he is worth helping, and that he can be helped.

Often one of the most important services a person can render in helping an alcoholic is to bring his relatives and friends to a sympathetic understanding of his problem and his needs. Their influence in the situation is sometimes a large factor in determining its outcome. If they should repudiate and turn against the alcoholic sufferer, perhaps because of the way he has humiliated and hurt his family, his chagrin may lead to an intensification of his problem. If, however, they do not reject him but extend to him their affection and care because they are aware of the true nature of his affliction, their encouragement may help him to make the turn toward recovery. Their understanding interest and support may be also a needed source of strength for the family of the alcoholic, those who are in daily close association with the problem.

Special pains should be taken to help the children of an alcoholic to see the situation in a large and true perspective. Often they are the most tragically affected in a home where alcohol is a problem. They may be torn between a proper affection for their alcoholic parent and a deep disappointment and distrust related to his behavior. They may be ashamed because their home is not like the happy nonalcoholic homes of their friends. It is of great importance for them to understand that the one whose drinking has brought unhappiness into the family circle is the victim of an insidious disorder from which he can and probably will recover. For their own sakes, as well as for the sake of the ailing parent, they should be made to see that their attitude can be a vital factor in his recovery.

Literature about alcoholism can be used to help an alcoholic to recognize his condition and acknowledge his need of help. Books and pamphlets published or recommended by Alcoholics Anonymous are usually suited to this purpose.

However, one should never make the mistake of thrusting a book into an alcoholic's hand, or mailing it to him, or in any other way forcing it upon his attention. The alcoholic resents being pushed into doing something about his problem. His sensitiveness in this matter should be taken into consideration in every effort to help him.

One who is close to an alcoholic will know how to provide him with literature on the subject of alcoholism. The wife of a man who is addicted to alcohol may, for example, secure a copy of AA's Big Book, *Alcoholics Anonymous,* begin to read it herself, and then leave it in a chair or on a table where her husband will find it. She will be careful not to disturb him while he examines the book or to appear to notice his interest in it. She will not talk about the book until he mentions it, and then she will let him take the lead in discussing its contents.

A lawyer whose wife showed unmistakable signs of alcoholism included several AA pamphlets and other suitable literature in a stack of papers on his desk at home. Then he had his secretary phone her for information she could get only by going through the things on her husband's desk. In this way he was able to get her to read selected literature on alcoholism that she would have resented and rejected if he had given it to her directly. The method was devious but successful.

The point is that the alcoholic must come to his own unforced conclusion about the nature of his problem. The turning point is his decision that he needs and wants help, and the decision must be his very own.

It needs hardly to be said that no effort should be made to provide an alcoholic with reading material unless he is relatively sober and able to use it with concentration and understanding.

It is of great importance for a person who is close to an alcoholic sufferer to know when and how to call in outside help in the person of a minister, a trusted family friend, or a member of Alcoholics Anonymous.

Not many persons are qualified to provide counsel and assistance in situations involving alcoholism. Care should be taken in selecting a counselor who knows what alcoholism is and how alcoholics should be treated, who is sympathetic and understanding in his relations to the afflicted person, and who is interested enough to give the case the time it requires.

Often the minister of the family in which alcoholism occurs is prepared to give the needed assistance. Or if he is not ready, he may help the family to get in touch with someone, perhaps from AA, who has the required knowledge and skill. The same can be said for the family physician, for a social worker, or for a trusted family friend. A direct appeal to an Alcoholics Anonymous group will usually bring good results. In most communities the best counselors in matters pertaining to alcoholism are members of AA, who know the problem from the inside and who are committed to helping other alcoholics.

It is usually wise to select and get in touch with someone who can give counsel and assistance well in advance of the time when the alcoholic, who is the object of concern, is ready to turn to an outsider for help. The wife of an alcoholic, for example, needs to talk to an understanding counselor as soon as she realizes that her husband's drinking is seriously out of control. His advice as to how she should deal with her husband and how she can handle situations that arise may be very helpful. Together they can lay plans for bringing the counselor into contact with the alcoholic, and for leading her husband to the realization that he needs and must seek help. Moreover, the wife can talk over with the counselor her own worries and resentments. If these are harbored and concealed, they may eventually make her as much of a problem as her husband.

How do we select a minister with whom to counsel about an alcohol problem? How may we discover whether or not a minister is ready to help in this kind of case? His preaching on the subject of alcohol is bound to be a clue to his interest and skill in the field of alcoholism. Sermons dealing with this problem, however, are a rather infrequent occurrence in most churches. We may learn how a minister has dealt with families in his parish where alcoholism has been a problem. Also, by his activities in the community in behalf of alcoholics or in connection with a local AA group, a minister may establish a reputation for being willing and helpful in dealing with this problem. Fortunate is the family whose own minister has the required knowledge and experience to make him an able counselor.

How do we make contact with a minister in order to seek his counsel and help? Simply by calling him up. We may ask him to visit us at his convenience or, better, to indicate a time when we can see him in his study. When making the appointment, we should indicate the general nature of our problem and the degree of urgency with which we seek help.

When we see the minister, we should not expect him to do all the talking or to give a lot of profound advice. The good counselor is first of all a good listener. He will expect us to do the talking. We should give him the full story and not withhold any relevant or useful information. We can be sure that he will not be shocked by anything we can tell him. He knows more about life than we do. Also, we can be sure that, as a good counselor and a minister, he will not betray any confidence.

Our talk with the minister will have three results. First, we will find in the interview a release from our emotional tensions. Our feelings of frustration, guilt, resentment, anger, fear, and hostility, all mingle to create this tension, and they must be talked out if the tension is to be relieved. Secondly, as we talk, we shall begin to have new insights and understandings about our problem. Our thoughts will become clearer. We shall begin to see our situation from the outside. Thirdly, the counselor will give us some guidance, mostly by quiet suggestion, in handling our responsibilities and in dealing with situations as they arise. He will put us in touch with further resources.

The caution needs to be repeated against calling in someone to talk to an alcoholic about what he is doing to his family and how he ought to straighten up. It is often possible, however, for a person who understands alcoholism and alcoholic behavior, such as a trained minister or a member of AA, to be of real help to an alcoholic even though he is called in prematurely.

A woman whose husband had been drinking heavily for several days during one of a series of periodic benders phoned her minister in the middle of the night. She tearfully related some of the sordid details of the current situation and then urged him to come to talk with her husband. The minister wisely told her that it would be better for him not to talk with her husband that night. He asked her to convey to her husband his own very sincere greetings and to tell him that he would be glad to see him in his study the next morning or at any convenient time. Three days later the alcoholic husband sought out the minister and with his help eventually established himself in sobriety.

Occasionally it is necessary for a person who is working with an alcoholic to take drastic action that may seem to be entirely negative in character. The wife of an alcoholic, for example, may have to call the police to protect herself and the children when her husband is abusively and dangerously drunk. Or the home situation may become so impossibly difficult that she finds it necessary to leave him. A man may be forced to place his alcoholic wife in a sanitarium in order to be free to carry on his business.

In taking these measures one runs the risk of alienating himself from the one he is seeking to help. There are times, however, when personal safety, the welfare of the children, and the integrity of the home become primary considerations. Only those who are involved in the immediate situation can decide whether or not drastic steps are required.

One should never threaten an alcoholic with extreme action without really intending to carry it out. It is better not to threaten or warn at all, but to do what is required when the time comes.

Sometimes a rigorous measure has the positive effect of bringing an alcoholic to a realization of the depth of his problem and to a recognition of his need of help. Many an alcoholic sufferer has continued drinking as long as his family pampered him and protected him from the consequences of his behavior. He has come to his senses and made the turn toward recovery only when he has been forced to face the realities of his situation.

When an alcoholic begins to show an interest in getting on top of his problem, he should be encouraged to take the initiative. Those who are close to him and who are trying to help him should stay in the background. They may make suggestions as to the steps he should take, the people he should see, the assistance he should seek. But as far as possible they should let him make the decisions and undertake the arrangements.

The idea is that, even when he has turned the corner toward recovery, he should not be made to feel that he is being forced or pushed into doing something about his problem. He continues to be very sensitive about his affliction, and may react badly to undue urging.

The steps an alcoholic is encouraged to take as he seeks sobriety may include the following: (1) He should discuss his problem with someone who is qualified to counsel with alcoholics, perhaps a minister or a member of AA with whom the family has already been in touch. (2) He should seek competent medical help where this seems to be in order. A period of hospitalization may be required. Many alcoholics need treatment for deficiency disorders related to prolonged excessive drinking. (3) He should make contact with Alcoholics Anonymous as the most useful agency working in the field of alcoholic rehabilitation. For most alcohol addicts the Twelve Steps of AA are a sure road to recovery. (4) If it seems to be necessary, he should seek the help of a competent psychiatrist or psychiatric counselor. (5) In due time he should be encouraged to attend services in the church of his choice.

In all these steps those who are nearest to him and most concerned about his recovery should be ready to counsel and assist. They should support him with their affection and encouragement. But they must let him take the initiative, make the decisions, and carry the responsibility as far as he is able.

Sometimes those who are close to an alcoholic need to be cautioned against resenting the part that others play in restoring him to sobriety. They seem to think that he should have made the grade for their sakes and with their help alone. They do not feel that way when a physical ailment, such as pneumonia, invades the family circle. Then they call in a medical doctor and rely upon him completely. They do not resent his services in bringing their loved one to recovery. No more should they resent the part that an AA group, for example, may take in helping someone near and dear to them to achieve a sober and useful life.

Do not expect an alcoholic to improve or recover quickly. Sometimes years pass, and patience is tried to the extreme, before the longed-for break comes. Often the road to recovery is long and hard. The alcoholic sufferer may be dry for months and suddenly go on a drinking spree. Relapses are tragic and serious, but they do not mean that the sufferer will not recover. Sometimes a "slip" is useful when it really convinces the alcoholic that he never again can touch alcohol. Bear with the alcoholic in his long struggle toward sobriety. Your help and encouragement mean more to him than he will ever be able to say, and his heart overflows with gratitude.

8

STRENGTH IN RELIGION

To live in daily close association with an alcoholic sufferer, to deal with him wisely and compassionately, always to do the right thing and never the wrong in handling situations as they arise, is no easy responsibility. The relationship requires on our part a double portion of understanding, patience, and strength. In this chapter let us consider some of the ways in which religion can be in us a resource and a power.

THE CENTRAL AFFIRMATION of Christian faith is the reality of God, the Maker and Sustainer of the universe. We believe in a living God, infinitely wise and good, within whose will all things exist. He is a great God, " his greatness is unsearchable," yet he " is nigh unto all them that call upon him." His laws and judgments stand over the affairs of men and nations, yet he is attentive to every man's need. For any man he can be " a very present help."

To believe in the living God is to believe that the universe embodies a divine purpose and plan. Life is full of disappointments and disasters that obscure the working of the eternal Will, like dark clouds that hide the sun. We confide in God, however, and in the ultimate fulfillment toward which all creation moves. This faith becomes meaningful and real when we see that in serving the needs of others, in helping men to live sober and useful lives, we become instruments of the beneficent purpose of God.

Christian faith assures us that the God who made us enfolds us in his love. He desires for every man only that which is good and right and lovely. The Father's compassion, so deeply expressed in the cross of Christ, embraces all men. Nothing can separate a person from the love of God. Here, truly, is the measure of man's worth and the high warrant for our endeavor in behalf of any man who has been hurt by alcohol.

Our belief in God implies that here is a source of help by which we can be patient and strong in meeting every situation. Anxieties and disappointments often attend our efforts to help an alcoholic friend or relative to achieve recovery. They are sometimes so severe and so prolonged that our own strength cannot bear them. Christian faith assures us that God supplies power adequate for all our needs. He will help us to be the kind of persons we ought to be in our relationships with alcohol's victims.

The most important means by which God's power and grace come into our lives is prayer. It is an instrument that we can use in the full assurance that God hears and answers. He knows our needs and his grace is sufficient. Prayer is seeking the help of God with the expectation that our quest will succeed.

Yet for many people praying is an unsatisfactory experience. Prayer has been the key to strength in the lives of great Christians in all ages, yet many have found it unrewarding and have given it up. Many others have been so uncertain as to how to proceed that they have never really started to pray.

For those who have difficulty in praying, there is help in reading the great prayers of others. These prayers in which are expressed the spiritual hungers and aspirations of the ages gradually become our own, and we ourselves commune with the loving Father to whom they are addressed. There is help too in the reading of selected Scripture portions and passages from other literature, both poetry and prose, which voice our need and enable us to realize the presence of the Most High, the indispensable condition of all praying. It is helpful also to have a regular time and place for communing with God and bringing to him our needs. As we pray in faith, seeking above all to know his will and to have grace to do it, so shall we be blessed and strengthened.

In the first book in this series, *My Faith Looks Up,* Russell Dicks points out that the task of prayer is not so much to enlist God's support for ourselves and our effort as it is to change our wills and desires so that they permit the power of God to flow over us, into us, and through us. God is not a dictator who bends us to his will, but a Creator, a Heavenly Father, who calls us to fellowship and to creative being, to become, as Paul has said, "heirs of God, and joint-heirs with Christ," who strengthens us.

A major resource of religion is the church itself, with its worship and fellowship. As we attend its services and join with others in communion with God, our hearts are strengthened, our spirits are lifted, and we are encouraged in our Christian responsibilities. In public worship as well as in private prayer, God is able to mediate to us his grace and power.

The fellowship of the church extends beyond the formal service of public worship. It often becomes deeper and richer as we take our places in the formal and informal group activities that are a large part of the life of every church. Here we may find friends who understand our problems and are able to help us in meeting them. In these groups too we may acquire interests and engage in tasks that enrich our lives and compensate in part for the sacrifices we must make in order to help someone near and dear to achieve sobriety. We may even find others who face problems that are similar to our own, who like us are seeking to help an alcoholic friend or relative.

An important result of being part of a church fellowship is that it brings the minister into a unique relationship with us and our problem. It enables us to take him into our confidence, to seek his advice and counsel, to call upon him when things get out of hand. He can be especially helpful in leading us to the wellsprings by which our own spiritual strength is replenished.

Something should be said about the responsibility of the churches in connection with the problems raised by the use of alcoholic beverages. Churches cannot be passive when men and women are brought through drinking to ruin and tragedy, or when alcoholic indulgence on the part of a few affects the well-being of many. The consequences of drinking in personal life and in social relations are such that churches are bound to be concerned.

Christian churches have certain resources that make them peculiarly qualified to deal constructively with the alcohol problem — a sense of the supreme worth of human life, an appreciation of the spiritual and moral possibilities of every individual, a vision of life as it should be lived, an awareness of man's duty to his fellow men, a keen sense of right and wrong, a deep sympathy with all who suffer, a mandate to proclaim God's judgment upon the ways of men, a fellowship wherein the followers of Christ worship together and help one another.

The law of love as defined and illustrated in the New Testament is for Christians the rule of life. It applies constantly to all personal and social conduct. Prior assumptions are man's inherent worth as a child of God, his inadequacy apart from God, and the essential brotherhood of all men. The ethic of love should be the churches' guide in dealing with all aspects of the alcohol problem.

A genuine concern for alcoholics and excessive drinkers, and for their families, is appropriate to the nature and function of the churches. Some antialcohol groups and their leaders seem to be so anxious to remove alcohol from society that they look upon efforts in behalf of the victims of alcohol as a denial of their goal. Such an attitude is at once unrealistic and inhumane. Churches, embodying the compassion of Christ, cannot withhold concern from those who are hurt by alcohol.

There are several ways in which a church can express its concern for alcoholics and other victims of alcohol.

1. The minister should be ready, by inclination and training, to extend pastoral service to alcohol addicts, excessive drinkers, and their families.

2. The minister should have firsthand acquaintance with all resources in the community for dealing with all aspects of the alcohol problem.

3. Other officers and workers in the church should know something of the resources in the church and in the community for helping the victims of alcohol.

4. In some churches it is possible to set up an advisory committee to counsel and assist the minister in his pastoral work with problem drinkers and their families. The committee may include a doctor, a member of AA, a psychologist or psychiatrist, a lawyer, a social worker, an educator.

5. The church can offer to provide a meeting place and other facilities for a local AA group.

6. By occasional references to the problem of alcoholism in his sermons and in church periodicals and communications to members, the minister should let the church and community know of his concern with the problem and his readiness to help.

7. The minister and the church should encourage the setting up and the strengthening of services in the community, both public and private, for the care and rehabilitation of alcoholics.

Excessive drinking is only one aspect of the alcohol problem. Moderate drinking too has social and moral implications that make it a concern of the churches.

It is not surprising that churches and church leaders generally, and especially in the evangelical Protestant tradition, advocate total abstinence from alcoholic beverages. They base their case against drinking on four considerations: (1) The moderate use of alcoholic beverages is sometimes an introduction to problem drinking. Present data suggest that 1 in 13 of all who begin to drink will become a problem to himself and to others because of alcohol. (2) Moderation provides the environment for problem drinking, the setting in which inebriety occurs. If it were not for the vast number of moderate users of alcoholic beverages, the liquor traffic could not exist. It is they who keep the problem active. (3) Moderate drinkers are the major influence in recruiting new drinkers. Nobody is ever persuaded to drink by watching an excessive drinker. The terrific social pressures which are such a factor in present-day drinking originate with those who are moderate users of alcoholic beverages. (4) Even moderate amounts of alcohol can affect a person's efficiency and behavior in such a way as to cause trouble. Beyond a doubt, many automobile accidents are caused by persons who are very mildly under alcoholic influence.

These considerations alone suggest that it is prudent to abstain completely from alcoholic beverages. The Christian ideal, however, goes far beyond the counsel of prudence. We all are "bound in the bundle of life." Christians are expected to help others to live at their best. At very least, this is required: "that no man put a stumblingblock or an occasion to fall in his brother's way." In view of all the trouble caused by drinking, many believe that nothing less than voluntary total abstinence can be truly consonant with the spirit of Christianity.

In these pages we have been concerned only with the problem of alcohol addiction. We have looked at the problem from the point of view of the person who is close to an alcoholic by ties of family or friendship. We have considered some of the things we should know about the affliction and some of the ways we can help a person who suffers from it.

The wife of a recovered alcoholic wrote to her minister a year after her husband had taken his last drink: " I often think of the years before he stopped drinking, especially the last four years when he was drunk, it seemed, most of the time. I remember when he lost his job, when he had his accident, when he disappeared for three weeks. I remember that things were often pretty rough at home — for him, for me, for the two children. It all seems like a bad dream now. I'm glad I didn't leave him. I'm glad I kept up my church association. I thank God for the friends who helped me to see the problem for what it was, and to say and do the right things. The happiest day of my life was when Jim told me that he had talked with you and that together you were going to work things out. He said that with God's help and your encouragement he was never going to drink again. He had made promises before, and he had meant every one of them. But this was different — it wasn't a promise, it was a statement of fact. This has been a most wonderful year. Jim is happy in his new work. He is really a new person in every way. I am no longer afraid for him or for our home."

Her joy was shared by her pastor and by a host of friends and relatives. A very ill person had returned to health.

PART
II
HELP FROM ALCOHOLICS

9

GUIDANCE FROM RECOVERED ALCOHOLICS

The following meditations are based on articles that have appeared in The A.A. Grapevine, *the official publication of Alcoholics Anonymous. Four of the articles were written by recovered alcoholics, one by the wife of a recovered alcoholic.*

These articles are used with permission of The A.A. Grapevine. *Their use here does not imply any sponsorship or authorization of this book on the part of Alcoholics Anonymous.*

Each meditation includes, in addition to the Grapevine *article, an introductory statement, a reading from the Bible, and a prayer.*

Spiritual Resources in AA

THE AA PROGRAM OF RECOVERY incorporates important techniques for spiritual growth — recognition of our inadequacy, belief in a Power greater than ourselves, moral inventory, confession of wrongs and shortcomings, making amends to others, prayer and meditation, and helping others. The Program can be used by relatives and friends of an alcoholic as a way to spiritual poise and power. This is the conviction of the wife of one of the founders of Alcoholics Anonymous.

Bill

It is hard to say just when Alcoholics Anonymous began. It may have been at the time a friend came to see my husband, Bill. Or it may have been at the moment of Bill's spiritual experience. Most AA's feel it is the time six months later when he met Dr. Bob in Akron, and, together, they started to help other alcoholics who wanted to be rid of their addiction.

But for me it was the day I first saw the released expression on my husband's face. We had been married seventeen years, and were compatible and companionable. Our interests were similar and we both deeply desired and strove for the other's welfare. The only, but considerable, block to our happiness was Bill's uncontrolled drinking. In the early years he said that he could stop when he wanted to and I thought I'd soon be able to make life so complete for him that he would wish to quit drinking entirely. Much later, when he really did want to stop, he was absolutely unable to do so, and we both then became terribly confused and frustrated. Oddly enough, he had been in other matters a person of strong will power, but his will seemed to melt away where alcohol was concerned. In his remorse and disappointment he was a tragic and heartbreaking figure. I too felt myself a failure, for despite every endeavor I had not been able to help him in time, nor could I aid him in the least in his final struggle for freedom.

Today I can talk and write about these intimate details of our life together. While Bill was drinking, I dared not even speak to my family about it and tried to hide the fact of his alcoholism in every way possible. Now that I have learned that Bill was actually a very sick man, that awful feeling of disgrace has left me. I have also learned how much help the telling of such experiences can be to those who are going through similar ones.

After Bill left the hospital for the last time, he began to think of the thousands of alcoholics who wanted to be rid of their malady. If they could be made to feel desperate enough, they might have a releasing experience just like his. He would hold before them the medical verdict that alcoholism was hopeless. So tirelessly, day and night, we worked. Our home was filled with alcoholics in various stages of sobriety. As many as five of them lived with us at one time. But none of them stayed sober for long. Then started a long process of trial and error; certain ideas were retained, but many discarded.

It was in June, 1935, that Bill went to Akron, Ohio, on a business trip. The venture failed. He finally contacted Dr. Bob, an Akron surgeon, soon to become cofounder of Alcoholics Anonymous. Bob too wanted above all to stop drinking. He and his wife, Anne, had done everything they could.

Something passed between these two men. There was real mutuality this time. By example they showed how it worked. Thus AA spread like a chain letter.

Bill had learned a great deal. At first he had tried to put every alcoholic he met in the way of a spiritual experience just like his own. As AA grew, he realized that what had come to him in a few dramatic minutes usually dawns on others in months or years. Sometimes the alcoholic himself does not even realize his own development, though his words and actions soon speak for him, for he is doing now what, of himself, he was unable to do before. He is gaining a serenity, a joy in living.

Watching Bill and the other men at the meetings, I noticed that many of them had begun to grow by leaps and bounds. This made me look at myself. I had been given a sound religious upbringing and felt I had done for Bill all a good wife could do, although this was strangely mixed with a sense of failure. At first it never occurred to me that I too needed spiritual development. I did not realize that by living such an abnormal life I might have become twisted, losing a sense of true values. After a while I saw that unless I jumped on the band wagon too, I would be left way behind. The AA Program I found could be most helpful to the nonalcoholics as well, a fact thousands of alcoholics' relatives and friends now apply to their own lives.

These Clinton Street days are full of memories. Some of them are humorous, some tragic. But most of them bring back a warm glow of hope and courage, of friendship and rebirth. For the fellowship in AA is unique. Ties are made overnight that it would take years to develop elsewhere. No one needs a false front. All barriers are down. Some who have felt outcasts all their lives, now know they really belong. From feeling as if they were dragging anchor through life, they suddenly sail free before the wind. For now they can be of tremendous and peculiar use to others having a dire need like their own.

By Lois.

(Bill is the cofounder of Alcoholics Anonymous. Lois is his wife.)

—*From* The A.A. Grapevine, *February, 1950.*

Bible Readings

" I appeal to you therefore, brethren, by the mercies of God, to present your bodies as a living sacrifice, holy and acceptable to God, which is your spiritual worship. Do not be conformed to this world but be transformed by the renewal of your mind, that you may prove what is the will of God, what is good and acceptable and perfect." Rom. 12:1, 2.

" God is our refuge and strength,
   A very present help in trouble.
   Therefore will not we fear." Ps. 46:1, 2.
" I will lift up mine eyes unto the hills,
   From whence cometh my help.
   My help cometh from the Lord,
   Which made heaven and earth." Ps. 121:1, 2.

"Happy is he that hath the God of Jacob for his help,
  Whose hope is in the Lord his God." Ps. 146:5.
"We know that in everything God works for good with
those who love him, who are called according to his purpose."
Rom. 8:28.
"My God will supply every need of yours according to his
riches in glory in Christ Jesus." Phil. 4:19.
"Let us then with confidence draw near to the throne of
grace, that we may receive mercy and find grace to help in time
of need." Heb. 4:16.

Prayer

Almighty and all-loving God, who art near unto us and dost
  support us, who proclaimest liberty to the captives and free-
  dom to prisoners:
Give us release from the forces that beset us.
As we contemplate thy goodness, help us to know how far we
  fall short of the good life to which thou hast called us in
  Christ.
In thy presence may we know our shortcoming and our need.

Forgive us for the things we remember with shame and peni-
  tence — our uncontrollable tempers, our shuffling insinceri-
  ties, the fears of our hearts, the lusts and leanings of our
  souls.
Forgive us for the moments that are beyond recall — the times
  of cruel passion, the betrayals of love and trust, the decep-
  tions and follies that resulted in wasted opportunities, the un-
  heeded fading of our dreams.
Forgive us for the moments that brought pain and disappointment to others — the careless word, the unjust condem-
  nation, the unfair judgment, the heartless criticism, the inconsiderate deed.

O Thou who knowest that we have no power of our own to
save ourselves, who alone can turn us from unholy desires
and degrading practices:

Cleanse our hearts.

Renew our wills.

Strengthen us to live sober and righteous lives and be ac-
counted worthy to be partakers of thy eternal Kingdom.

Through the grace and merit of Jesus Christ, our Lord. Amen.

ONE DAY AT A TIME

An AA member will often use the " twenty-four-hour plan "
in dealing with his problem. He will set out to remain sober
and to practice the AA principles for twenty-four hours, one
day at a time. At the beginning of each day he will seek God's
help " just for today."

Many who use the " twenty-four-hour plan " testify that it
keeps them from slipping into a false sense of sufficiency and
security, which for alcoholics is a fatal deception, and that it
keeps them close to God, who alone can give them mastery
over their problem.

The plan commends itself to all who seek victory over stubborn personal faults and evil habits. Here truly is one of the
secrets of successful living — making the most and the best of
each day.

You Have Today

Did it ever occur to you that today is actually the only day
that really concerns you? It is the one day at your disposal, the
one day in which you can think and plan and work.

It is surprising how many people live as if yesterday or tomorrow were the only time worthy of their attention. Those
who turn toward yesterday often live in remorse for acts done

that should have been left undone, for words spoken that had better been left unspoken, for opportunities rejected, for slights experienced, or for some failure of long ago. People live in yesterday when they bemoan the passing of the "good old times," when they imagine that good has gone from them beyond recall. They live in the emptiness of nebulous dreams; they have lost contact with the solid ground of reality.

Then there are those who see tomorrow as their only day, the day when they are to solve their problems, perform their duties, make their self-improvement, attain their goals, find their happiness.

Or perhaps they look upon tomorrow with apprehension and fears, seeing in it the coming of chaos or bitterness, until they shrivel up with a feeling of hopeless inadequacy.

Those who live in yesterday live in the grave of the dead past, in a time that has gone forever. Those who live in tomorrow live in a day not yet born, in a fantasy empty of life.

But today is our day! It is the only day worth living in, the only day worth giving attention to. The sands of yesterday have been washed away by the seas of time, but the rock of today is firmly beneath our feet. Today is within our grasp, plastic to our touch. Today we can speak the kind word, do the good deed, accept our opportunity, live up to our best. Today we can forgive and forget the past and forge ahead in our new way of life. Our very real good is in today, for out of it we can make heavenly conditions.

The fruit we wish to pick tomorrow lies hidden in the seed of today. The goals we are to reach and the problems we are to solve tomorrow depend upon today's diligence, hope, faith, and today's conviction of the almightiness of good.

— *From* The A.A. Grapevine, *June, 1951.*

Bible Readings

" Boast not thyself of to-morrow;

For thou knowest not what a day may bring forth."
Prov. 27:1.

" Give us this day our daily bread." Matt. 6:11.

" This is the day which the Lord hath made;

We will rejoice and be glad in it." Ps. 118:24.

" Behold, now is the acceptable time; behold, now is the day
of salvation." II Cor. 6:2.

" Therefore do not be anxious about tomorrow, for tomorrow will be anxious for itself. Let the day's own trouble be
sufficient for the day." Matt. 6:34.

Prayer

Most gracious Father, who art never far from any of us and
art found by them that diligently seek thee:

We thank thee for thy mercies which are new each day.

Help us to recognize thy goodness in the world about us, in the
lives of men and women we meet, in the leadings of thy
spirit.

We would not go forth without thy guidance to the tasks of
the day.

Strengthen us so that in our work we may be faithful; in suffering, patient; amid trials, courageous; under disappointment,
full of hope.

Help us this day to have victory over the things that keep us
from being our best.

Teach us to put to good account whatever talents thou hast
given us, and enable us to redeem our time by patience and
zeal.

Reveal to us thy will, O God; show us thy way and give us
power to walk in it.
Fulfill in us and through us thy purpose.
Be thou our Guard and our Guide, this day and forevermore.
Through Jesus Christ, our Lord. Amen.

Overcoming Fear

Fear may be defined as a painful feeling of impending danger, evil, trouble, or disaster. In varied subtle shades and forms,
fear is often the seedbed in which alcoholism takes root. For
many alcoholics permanent recovery is possible only when
fears are recognized, analyzed, and then transformed. Here is
a formula that all of us can use in dealing with our fears.

A Vague Apprehension

Ralph Waldo Emerson once said, " A man is what he thinks
about all day long." Obviously a man thinks about many things
in the course of a day. But, says Emerson, beneath all these
thoughts is one primary or fundamental thought, into which
all his other thoughts are drained, and from which they take
their color and content.

Fear, for example, begins as a thin trickle of worry across the
mind — just a vague apprehension. Repeated, it has the tend-
ency to cut deeper into the consciousness, until presently you
have a great stream of fear running through the mind, and into
this stream of fear — into this primary fear thought — all your
other thoughts are drained. Fear is at the heart of the alcoholic's problem. Until it is overcome, there is little chance of
recovery.

What is fear? Of course fear has many faces, but from the
standpoint of the alcoholic, what is fear? Well, just look at the
word itself. To the alcoholic, the " f " of fear represents the

thousands of *frustrations* of which he is conscious and which have plagued his days and made sleepless his nights. The " e " of fear constantly brings him face to face with himself and the *egomania* of which he has been possessed, which has expressed itself in selfishness and utter disregard of others. The " a " of fear reminds him of the twin demons *anger* and *anxiety,* who not only moved in but almost invariably took possession of the citadel of his being and wrecked his normal thought processes. And the " r " of fear always speaks to him of the *resentments* he cherishes, often nourishing them as though they were virtues.

Our hope lies in the transformation of fear. So long as we, as alcoholics, are dominated by fear, our chances of recovery are very small. It can be done, and by the Grace of God it has been done. The " f " of fear can be transformed into *faith,* faith in God, faith in ourselves, and faith in our fellows. The " e " of fear can be changed to *endeavor,* for when we come to believe something strongly enough we will try to do something about it and no man ever tried sincerely and failed in the end. The " a " of fear can become *accomplishment,* for with faith and endeavor, accomplishment must follow as the night and day, we cannot fail. And last, but most important, the " r " of fear can brighten into *repose,* which is just another word for peace of mind. Yes, even an alcoholic can saddle the mustang called fear and ride it down the road to happiness.

— From The A.A. Grapevine, *August, 1950.*

Bible Readings

" I sought the Lord, and he heard me,

And delivered me from all my fears." Ps. 34:4.

" I will trust, and not be afraid:

For the Lord Jehovah is my strength and my song." Isa. 12:2.

"God did not give us a spirit of timidity but a spirit of power and love and self-control." II Tim. 1:7.

"There is no fear in love, but perfect love casts out fear. For fear has to do with punishment, and he who fears is not perfected in love." I John 4:18.

Prayer

Most holy and merciful God, who dost teach us to dread nothing but the loss of thee, and to cast all our cares upon thee:

Save us from faithless fears and worldly anxieties that dim the light of our souls.

Cast from our minds the worries and apprehensions that becloud our lives and hide us from the light of thy love.

Give us the spirit of trust so that all fear and foreboding may be cast out, and that right reason and calm assurance may rule our thoughts and wills.

May quietness and confidence be our strength.

Teach us to take thy hand in the darkness, and to hear thy voice: "Fear not, for I am with thee. I have called thee by thy name."

Lead us into the secret of thy peace, which quiets every misgiving and fills the heart with joy and confidence.

Through Jesus Christ, our Lord. Amen.

Easy Does It

A good deal of the philosophy of Alcoholics Anonymous is gathered up in the slogan, "Easy Does It." The idea is that an alcoholic gets nowhere in his search for sobriety until he stops straining. He doesn't have to fight the world in order to keep dry. He reaches his desire not by struggle but by surrender. He turns his will and life over to the care of God. He lets God take over. He stops trying to be somebody. He drops all pretension and begins to be himself. This same attitude and practice will do just as much for a nonalcoholic as for an alcoholic person.

First Things First

" Don't " is a horrid word! It has no place in the bright lexicon of an alcoholic. However, Charlie S., of Greenwich Village, New York, has found some " don't's " that have changed his whole outlook on life. They are not " don't's " as in " Don't do this," or " Don't do that," but, as Charlie says, " a personal list of things I've discovered I don't have to do."

AA has taught me that I don't have to drink. That was only the beginning. As my thinking cleared up, I began to realize that there were many things I didn't have to do — that my whole life had been hemmed in by other obsessions quite as strong as my drinking.

Today I am pretty well free of trying to live up to a bunch of phony ideas and screwy ideals. What a blessed relief! Here is a partial list of " don't have to's ":

I don't have to live in the biggest house, have the best job, wear only tailor-made clothes, drive the flashiest car. These are some of the material ideas left over from my illusion that I had to be a big operator. True, I seldom had any of those things. But I was bound by them, tormented and frustrated because I didn't have them, and increasingly resentful, viciously so, because down deep I knew I never should have them. But these are the least important of my " don't have to's " today.

I also found I don't have to pretend. I don't even have to strain. I don't have to lie, be a petty cheat, or run away — not from anything. And best of all, I don't have to hate myself, secretly, way down deep inside. No, the pressure's off now. Today, my job is not the top dog in my profession. But it's a good job and I do it efficiently, well within the limits of my talents and abilities. My apartment is small. But it's the first home I've had in twenty-five years. My car is a plain sedan, but it gets me where I want to go. My ready-made suits fit very well.

But the changes inside are the important ones. When I quit trying to be somebody I thought I had to be, I began to be the kind of guy I really am. And not such a bad fellow, at that! When I stripped away the phoniness, I found a pretty decent man, simple, and, at long last, humble!

When I think back on the ridiculous things I thought I had to do, had to be, I wonder how any grown man could be so childish. The meaning of life itself has changed for me. Oddly enough, since I've quit straining, since I've discovered my "don't have to's," my chances of acquiring some of those material things are better than they ever were before. But even if none of that comes to pass, I know now I can live a decent life, a useful and constructive one. And the only things I have to be are sober, humble, honest, and willing!

— *From* The A.A. Grapevine, *September, 1949.*

Bible Readings

" In returning and rest shall ye be saved;

In quietness and in confidence shall be your strength." Isa. 30:15.

" The work of righteousness shall be peace;

And the effect of righteousness, quietness and assurance for ever." Isa. 32:17.

" Therefore I tell you, do not be anxious about your life, what you shall eat or what you shall drink, nor about your body, what you shall put on. Is not life more than food, and the body more than clothing? Look at the birds of the air: they neither sow nor reap nor gather into barns, and yet your heavenly Father feeds them. Are you not of more value than they? And which of you by being anxious can add one cubit to his span of life? And why be anxious about clothing? Consider the lilies of the field, how they grow; they neither toil nor spin; yet I tell you, even Solomon in all his glory was not arrayed like one of these. But if God so clothes the grass of the field, which today is alive and tomorrow is thrown into the oven, will he not much more clothe you, O men of little faith? Therefore do not be anxious, saying, ' What shall we eat? ' or ' What shall we drink? ' or ' What shall we wear? ' For the Gentiles seek all these things; and your heavenly Father knows that you need them all. But seek first his kingdom and his righteousness, and all these things shall be yours as well." Matt. 6:25-33.

" But the Lord answered her, ' Martha, Martha, you are anxious and troubled about many things; one thing is needful. Mary has chosen the good portion, which shall not be taken away from her.' " Luke 10:41, 42.

Prayer

Almighty God, who hast called us to a life that grows hard only when we fail in wisdom and devotion:
Grant that we may find our highest good in thy service.

Thou art the light of our hearts, the life of our souls, the strength of our minds.
From our narrow and limited world we would pass into thy greater world.
From our petty and miserable selves we would escape to thee, to find in thee the power and freedom of a larger life.

Save us from pretension and pride.
Give us a vision of the abundant life to which thou dost call us in Christ.

Help us to walk in paths of purity and sincerity, to renounce
the hidden things of dishonesty, and to have no commerce
with the works of darkness.

Let thy light fill our hearts more and more, until we become in
truth the children of light, and perfectly at one with thee.
Through Jesus Christ, our Lord. Amen.

Patience and Understanding

The attitude of the members of an alcoholic's family is often
a factor of critical importance in bringing about his recovery.
Their quiet patience and understanding are a constant encouragement for him to do something about his problem.
Many a recovered alcoholic is deeply grateful for his family's
helpful attitude in the years of his sojourn in the far country.
Even a teen-age son can help his alcoholic mother to come to
herself.

My Son Had the Answer

Once in a while, a nonalcoholic husband or wife or sister
asks me how to be helpful to the family alcoholic. Sometimes
the question comes in simple sincerity, sometimes with an understandable righteous and cynical gleam in the eye.

I do my best to answer, depending on the circumstances and
on the person. But it's a hard question for me, because it strikes
too nearly home. I know the answer too well, and know how
hard a set of precepts it must be to follow. When I think of the
perfect helpful family attitude, I think of my son.

I was an odd sort of periodic drunk. I had long bad bouts,
and good times. The pattern still shows after almost three sober
years — I still speed up and slow down, for no reason that I
understand, although liquor is no longer part of the picture.

The long bad bouts usually went with periods of frenzied work, such frenzied work that my bosses unfortunately let me get by with murder. I was a nervous wreck and I was hard to get along with, but I turned out more ideas and wrote more copy when plastered than the steadier-paced produced stone sober.

The frenzy did not go home with me after office hours. Gloom did and a bottle. I used to gobble up dinner somehow, and then lie down and brood.

My son was twelve during one of the blackest of these episodes. Nobody ever had to tell him the bottle was a symptom of illness. He never thought anything different. He never acted anything different. Once he bawled me out; once he said, " I think it's partly your psychological attitude, Mother, that makes you so tired." He used to hunt for things like P.T.A. meetings for me to go to, without a word about filling evenings for me with something better than liquor and moping. I used to manage to turn up at them, sober, if it killed me, which it usually very nearly did.

But there was little reproach and no scorn and no infant righteousness. Just sympathy, for the authentic illness he never questioned, and encouragement to do other things, otherwise. Not laid on so thick as to be obvious, either.

During the good times, when I managed for months at a time not to drink at all, he relaxed. Never a word about the bad time past; never a word about another bad time probably coming. Because of the never-a-word, we share nice memories.

He was away for a month's visit when I started on the Program. He was sixteen then. When he came back, I said, " I joined Alcoholics Anonymous while you were gone."

He said: " I'm glad. I've been worried about you. Is that why you look so happy? "

No further comment. Again no mention of the bad times

past. We started fresh from there.

I was a distressingly eager beaver in my early days on the Program, and I know he got bored to tears with my zeal. He told me as much later. But he never said a word of protest. He listened. He tried to find out what the Program was all about without a suggestion from me; he took, and adapted for himself, as much as a nonalcoholic can use — which is most of it. He has learned to think his way through and out the other side of resentments; he does not criticize; he lives just in today, which is a good lesson for a kid who loves college as much as he does, and who well may be drafted at any moment. I didn't tell him to; he learned along with me.

He too is happy, quite possibly happier than if his odd, fond mother had been some kind of neurotic other than alcoholic. For he knows that the most depressing stories can have good endings. He has the kind of faith that comes, as it can to the nonalcoholics who love us, from seeing miracles, and from helping them to happen.

— *From* The A.A. Grapevine, *April, 1951.*

Bible Readings

"When he came to himself he said, . . . 'I will arise and go to my father, and I will say to him, "Father, I have sinned against heaven and before you; I am no longer worthy to be called your son; treat me as one of your hired servants."' And he arose and came to his father. But while he was yet at a distance, his father saw him and had compassion, and ran and embraced him and kissed him." Luke 15:17-20.

"Brethren, if a man is overtaken in any trespass, you who are spiritual should restore him in a spirit of gentleness. Look to yourself, lest you too be tempted. Bear one another's burdens, and so fulfill the law of Christ." Gal. 6:1, 2.

"And be kind to one another, tenderhearted, forgiving one

another, as God in Christ forgave you." Eph. 4:32.

"Love is patient and kind; . . . Love does not insist on its own way; it is not irritable or resentful; it does not rejoice at wrong, but rejoices in the right. Love bears all things, believes all things, hopes all things, endures all things." I Cor. 13:4–7.

Prayer

O God, who hast called us for fellowship with one another, who hast bound us all together in mutual love and responsibility:

Teach us to think not of ourselves alone, but also of one another.

Make us sensitive, O God, to the needs of those with whom we live in family and community.

Open our eyes to see, and our hearts to feel, their joy and their sadness.

Help us to understand their burdens and trials, and increase our sympathy.

Take from us all pride and boasting, all narrowness and selfishness;

Make us gentle, considerate, kind, and patient.

Fill us with the compassion of Christ, so that we may be compassionate toward all whom we can help.

Through Jesus Christ, our Lord. Amen.